Math 7
A Reference Guide

outors

Specialist

uitor

Creative Director, Print and ePublishing

Williams   *Senior Print Visual Designer, Cover Designer*

Senior Visual Designer

dit, Charlotte Fullerton   *Media Editors*

Senior Manager, Writers and Editors

erner, Abhilasha Parakh   *Senior Project Managers*

omas   *Senior Director, Content and Assessment*

ngel   *Director, Mathematics Content Specialists*

lle Kitt   *Director, Instructional Design*

Golomb   *Senior Director, Program Management Product Development*

istopher Frescholtz   *Senior Director, Program Management*

sa Dimaio Iekel   *Director, Print Production and Manufacturing*

About K12 Inc.

K12 Inc., a technology-based education company, is the nation's leading provider of proprietary curriculum and online education programs to students in grades K–12. K^{12} provides its curriculum and academic services to online schools, traditional classrooms, blended school programs, and directly to families. K12 Inc. also operates the K^{12} International Academy, an accredited, diploma-granting online private school serving students worldwide. K^{12}'s mission is to provide any child the curriculum and tools to maximize success in life, regardless of geographic, financial, or demographic circumstances. K12 Inc. is accredited by CITA. More information can be found at www.K12.com.

ISBN: 978-1-60153-507-8 (online book)
ISBN: 978-1-60153-500-9 (printed book)

Printed by Quad Graphics, Versailles, KY, USA, May 2016

Contents

The Basics

Adding and Subtracting Rational Numbers

Multiplying and Dividing Rational Numbers

Ratios and Rates

Proportions

Expressions and Inequalities

Plane Figures

Circumference of Circles and Area

Three-Dinensional Geometry

Statistics

Probability

Appendices

K¹² Summit Curriculum

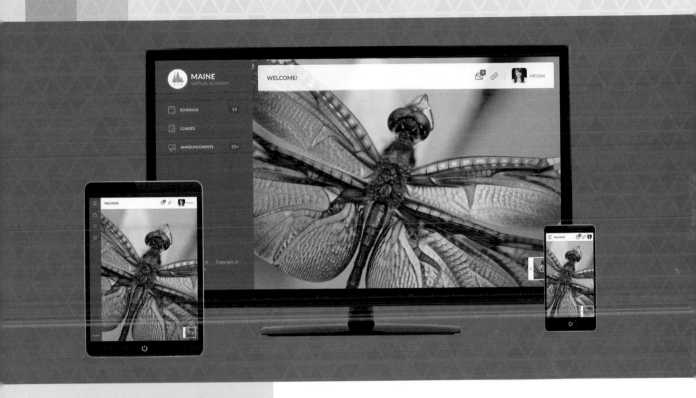

And remember: The pages in your book are also online!

Go to the online course to look for these digital resources in your lessons:

60 – second MATH

Videos will introduce you to each topic.

math CAST

Visual learning with animations and interaction will help you master key skills.

Worked EXAMPLE

Solve problems with the help of stepped examples.

APPLY it!

Use real-world examples to practice what you've learned.

The Basics

Let's start at the very beginning; it's a very good place to start. Just as you need to know basic grammar and vocabulary as you begin to learn any language, you need to know some basic building blocks as you begin to learn algebra.

Order of Operations

Addition, subtraction, multiplication, and division are operations.

When an expression has more than one operation, you must use the **order of operations** to simplify it. To **simplify a numerical expression** means to find its value.

Order of Operations Without Grouping

Step 1 Multiply and divide from left to right.

Step 2 Add and subtract from left to right.

▶ **Think About It** Simplifying a numerical expression means the same as evaluating a numerical expression.

Simplifying Expressions Without Grouping Symbols

EXAMPLE 1

Simplify.

A $1 + 2 \cdot 5$

SOLUTION

$1 + 2 \cdot 5 = 1 + \mathbf{10}$ Multiply.

$ = 11$ Add.

▶ **Think About It**

NOTATION • and × A raised dot and an × both mean multiplication.

B $6 \div 2 \cdot 3$

SOLUTION

$6 \div 2 \cdot 3 = \mathbf{3} \cdot 3$ Divide.

$\qquad\quad\ = 9$ Multiply.

C $5 \cdot 2 - 6 \div 2$

SOLUTION

$5 \cdot 2 - 6 \div 2 = \mathbf{10} - 6 \div 2$ Multiply.

$\qquad\qquad\ = 10 - \mathbf{3}$ Divide.

$\qquad\qquad\ = 7$ Subtract.

D $12 + 55 \div 5 - 2 \cdot 10 + 9$

SOLUTION

$12 + 55 \div 5 - 2 \cdot 10 + 9 = 12 + \mathbf{11} - 2 \cdot 10 + 9$ Divide.

$\qquad\qquad\qquad\qquad\ = 12 + 11 - \mathbf{20} + 9$ Multiply.

$\qquad\qquad\qquad\qquad\ = \mathbf{23} - 20 + 9$ Add.

$\qquad\qquad\qquad\qquad\ = \mathbf{3} + 9$ Subtract.

$\qquad\qquad\qquad\qquad\ = 12$ Add. ■

Simplifying Expressions with Grouping Symbols

Grouping symbols are symbols such as parentheses ( ), brackets [ ], and braces { }. Perform all operations inside grouping symbols first. If there is more than one set of grouping symbols in an expression, perform the operations in the innermost set of grouping symbols first.

Order of Operations with Grouping

Step 1 Perform operations within grouping symbols.

Step 2 Multiply and divide from left to right.

Step 3 Add and subtract from left to right.

EXAMPLE 2

Simplify.

A $5 \cdot (2 + 7)$

SOLUTION

$$5 \cdot (2 + 7) = 5 \cdot 9 \qquad \text{Add inside the grouping symbols.}$$
$$= 45 \qquad \text{Multiply.}$$

B $20 \div (10 \times 2)$

SOLUTION

$$20 \div (10 \times 2) = 20 \div 20 \qquad \text{Multiply inside the grouping symbols.}$$
$$= 1 \qquad \text{Divide.}$$

C $24 - \left[4 \cdot (6 - 5) + 5\right]$

SOLUTION

The parentheses are inside the brackets. Use the order of operations to simplify $6 - 5$ first.

$$24 - \left[4 \cdot (6 - 5) + 5\right] = 24 - \left[4 \cdot 1 + 5\right] \qquad \text{Subtract inside the parentheses.}$$
$$= 24 - \left[4 + 5\right] \qquad \text{Multiply inside the brackets.}$$
$$= 24 - 9 \qquad \text{Add inside the brackets.}$$
$$= 15 \qquad \text{Subtract.} \ \blacksquare$$

$$2A \quad 5 \cdot 2 + 7 = 10 + 7$$
$$= 17$$

$$2B \quad 20 \div 10 \times 2 = 2 \times 2$$
$$= 4$$

$$2C \quad 24 - 4 \cdot (6 - 5) + 5 = 20 + 5$$
$$= 25$$

Placing Grouping Symbols to Get a Specified Value

You can get different values for an expression by changing the placement of grouping symbols.

EXAMPLE 3

Place grouping symbols in the expression $90 - 10 \div 2 + 3$ to get expressions that have the values 16 and 82.

▶ **Think About It** Solve Example 3 by trial and error. Experiment by including different parts of the expression in parentheses.

SOLUTION

Get the value 16.

$$(90 - 10) \div (2 + 3) = 80 \div 5$$
$$= 16$$

Get the value 82.

$$90 - (10 \div 2 + 3) = 90 - (5 + 3)$$
$$= 90 - 8$$
$$= 82 \ \blacksquare$$

Simplifying Expressions with a Fraction Bar

The fraction bar represents division. It can be used as a grouping symbol.

EXAMPLE 4

Simplify.

A $\dfrac{60 \div 3}{2 + 2}$

SOLUTION

$\dfrac{60 \div 3}{2 + 2} = \dfrac{20}{4}$ Simplify the numerator and denominator separately.

$\phantom{\dfrac{60 \div 3}{2 + 2}} = 5$ Divide the numerator by the denominator.

▶ **Think About It** You can write the expression $\dfrac{60 \div 3}{2 + 2}$ as $(60 \div 3) \div (2 + 2)$.

B $\dfrac{3 \cdot (17 - 5)}{4 + 9 - 1}$

SOLUTION

Use the order of operations to simplify the numerator and denominator.

$\dfrac{3 \cdot (17 - 5)}{4 + 9 - 1} = \dfrac{3 \cdot 12}{4 + 9 - 1}$ In the numerator, subtract inside the parentheses.

$\phantom{\dfrac{3 \cdot (17 - 5)}{4 + 9 - 1}} = \dfrac{36}{12}$ In the numerator, multiply. In the denominator, add and subtract from left to right.

$\phantom{\dfrac{3 \cdot (17 - 5)}{4 + 9 - 1}} = 3$ Divide. ▪

Application: Business

EXAMPLE 5

A plumber charges \$25 to make a visit plus \$65/h. Suppose the plumber works on a project for a total of 3 h. Write and simplify an expression to find how much the plumber will charge for the project.

SOLUTION

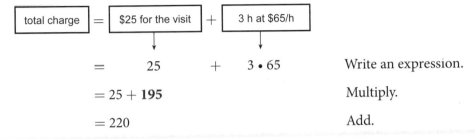

$$= \quad 25 \quad + \quad 3 \cdot 65 \qquad \text{Write an expression.}$$

$$= 25 + \mathbf{195} \qquad \text{Multiply.}$$

$$= 220 \qquad \text{Add.}$$

The plumber will charge \$220 for the project. ■

Variable Expressions

An **expression** is a group of mathematical symbols.

Expressions can contain numbers, variables, and operation symbols. A **numerical expression** consists of numbers and one or more operations.

A **variable** is a symbol that represents a value. In most cases, variables are letters, such as x, y, a, and n. Most variables are lowercase and italicized.

A **variable expression** consists of one or more variables and one or more operations; it may also contain numbers.

Numerical expressions do not contain variables. Variable expressions do.

Numerical expression	Variable expression
$8 - 6 \cdot (3 + 1)$	$8 - 6 \cdot (a + b)$
$\dfrac{25}{8 - 3}$	$\dfrac{x}{y - z}$

A numerical expression has only one value. But a variable expression can have different values, depending on the values that are substituted for its variables.

▶ **Think About It** *Vary* means "change." Thus, when a variable changes its value, the value of the expression changes, too.

Evaluating Expressions

To **evaluate a variable expression**, replace all the variables in the expression with numbers and simplify. Remember to use the order of operations when simplifying.

When working with variable expressions, there are a few ways to show multiplication. You may be used to using the multiplication $\times$, but in algebra, you will most often see a raised dot. Also, you can show multiplication by putting a number right next to a variable. For instance, $6a$ is the same as $6 \cdot a$ and $6 \times a$.

> ▶ **Remember** Multiplication can be shown in different ways. All of the following mean "six times the quantity three plus one":
> $$6(3 + 1)$$
> $$6 \cdot (3 + 1)$$
> $$6 \times (3 + 1)$$

EXAMPLE 1

A Evaluate $7n + 5$ when $n = 8$.

SOLUTION

$7n + 5 = 7 \cdot 8 + 5$	Substitute 8 for n.
$= 56 + 5$	Multiply.
$= 61$	Add.

B Evaluate $x - y + 2$ when $x = 11$ and $y = 3$.

SOLUTION

$x - y + 2 = 11 - 3 + 2$	Substitute 11 for x and 3 for y.
$= 8 + 2$	Subtract.
$= 10$	Add.

C Evaluate $\dfrac{c - 5d}{10 \cdot (2d + 1)}$ when $c = 200$ and $d = 4$.

SOLUTION

$$\frac{c - 5d}{10 \cdot (2d + 1)} = \frac{200 - 5 \cdot 4}{10 \cdot (2 \cdot 4 + 1)} \qquad \text{Substitute 200 for } c \text{ and 4 for } d.$$

$$= \frac{200 - 20}{10 \cdot 9} \qquad \text{Simplify the numerator and denominator separately.}$$

$$= \frac{180}{90}$$

$$= 2 \qquad \text{Divide.} \ \blacksquare$$

Application: Temperature

EXAMPLE 2

To approximate the temperature in degrees Celsius after an increase in altitude of f feet, you can use the expression $b - 2 \cdot \dfrac{f}{1000}$, where b is the beginning temperature. A hiker climbs 4000 ft to a summit from a parking lot, where it is 35°C. Approximate the temperature at the summit.

SOLUTION

$$b - 2 \cdot \frac{f}{1000} = 35 - 2 \cdot \frac{4000}{1000} \qquad \text{Substitute 35 for } b \text{ and 4000 for } f.$$

$$= 35 - 2 \cdot 4 \qquad \text{Divide.}$$

$$= 35 - 8 \qquad \text{Multiply.}$$

$$= 27 \qquad \text{Subtract.}$$

The temperature at the summit is about 27°C. ■

Application: Sports

EXAMPLE 3

The distance around a rectangle is its perimeter and is given by the expression $2l + 2w$, where l represents length and w represents width. Find the perimeter of a soccer field that is 100 yd long and 60 yd wide.

> ▶ **Think About It** Variables are often the first letters in the words they represent, such as l for length and w for width.

SOLUTION

$$2l + 2w = 2 \cdot 100 + 2 \cdot 60 \qquad \text{Substitute 100 for } l \text{ and 60 for } w.$$

$$= 200 + 120 \qquad \text{Multiply.}$$

$$= 320 \qquad \text{Add.}$$

The perimeter of the soccer field is 320 yd. ■

Writing Expressions for Word Phrases

To solve problems, you sometimes need to translate word phrases into variable expressions.

You can use the table to help determine what operation is indicated by a particular word phrase.

Matching Words and Phrases to Operations

Addition	Subtraction	Multiplication	Division
plus	minus	times	quotient
more than	less than	product	separate into
increased by	decreased by	of	equal groups
sum	difference	combine	
total	shorter	equal groups	
longer	younger		
older			

Think carefully when you translate. The phrases in the table do not automatically indicate particular operations. For example, "two is less than six" is written 2 < 6; there is no subtraction involved.

Translating Word Phrases into Variable Expressions

EXAMPLE 1

Translate the word phrase into a variable expression.

A the sum of 16 and a number

SOLUTION

Possible variable expression:

$16 + n$ The word *sum* indicates addition. Use any letter for the variable.

B 6 less than twice a number

SOLUTION

Possible variable expression:

$2x - 6$ To represent 6 *less than* a quantity, you need to subtract 6 from that quantity.
In this case, the quantity is twice a number, or 2 times a number.

C 20 students separated into equal groups

SOLUTION

Possible variable expression:

$\frac{20}{n}$ or $20 \div n$ You do not know how many equal groups, so use a variable for the
number of equal groups. Use division to separate into equal groups.

> ▶ **Think About It** Order matters in subtraction and division.
> In Example 1B, $6 - 2x$ is incorrect. In Example 1C, $\frac{n}{20}$ and $n \div 20$
> are incorrect.

D the number of seconds in *m* minutes

SOLUTION

Possible variable expression:

$60m$ You need to combine *m* "groups" of seconds with 60 in each group.
Use multiplication to combine equal groups. ▪

Translating Variable Expressions into Word Phrases

You can write a word phrase for a variable expression in more than one way.

EXAMPLE 2

Translate the variable expression into a word phrase.

A $m - 8$

SOLUTION
Possible answers include:

the difference of m and 8
8 less than m
m minus 8

B $bc + 2$

SOLUTION
Possible answers include:

the product of b and c, increased by 2
2 more than the product of b and c

C $b \cdot (c + 2)$

SOLUTION
Possible answers include:

the product of b and the sum of c and 2
b times the quantity c plus 2 ■

▶ **Think About It** Notice that the parentheses in Example 2C form an expression whose meaning is different from the expression in Example 2B.

Application: Age

EXAMPLE 3

A Sam's mom is 2 years older than 5 times Sam's age. Write a variable expression to represent the age of Sam's mom.

SOLUTION

Possible variable expression:

$5s + 2$ Let s represent Sam's age. To represent 2 years older, add 2. The word *times* indicates multiplication.

> ▶ **Remember** Expressions show relationships between different entities.

B The ages of three sisters are consecutive odd whole numbers. Write a variable expression to represent the age of the oldest sister if the age of the youngest sister is y.

> ▶ **Remember** Whole numbers are the numbers 0, 1, 2, 3, ...

SOLUTION

Consecutive whole numbers, such as 5 and 6, have no whole numbers between them. Consecutive odd whole numbers, such as 5 and 7, have no odd whole numbers between them.

Notice that to get from an odd whole number to the next consecutive odd whole number, you add 2. Therefore, the ages of the sisters are y, $y + 2$, and $y + 4$.

The variable expression for the age of the oldest sister is $y + 4$. ■

Related Equations

You can use related equations to solve equations.

If you start with 5 and add 2, the result is 7. If you subtract 2 from 7, the result is the number you started with: 5. A set of related equations all communicate the same relationship between three values, but in different ways. Any time you have an addition equation, you could write two subtraction equations that describe the same relationship between the values.

Related Equations for Addition and Subtraction

For any a, b, and c,

$$a + b = c$$
$$a = c - b$$
$$b = c - a$$

All three are related equations.

Example

$$5 + 2 = 7$$
$$5 = 7 - 2$$
$$2 = 7 - 5$$

All three are related equations.

Writing Related Equations for Addition and Subtraction

A good strategy for writing a set of related equations for addition and subtraction is to identify the sum and write the addition equation first. Then, to write the subtraction equations, subtract each different addend from the sum.

EXAMPLE 1

Write a complete set of related equations for the given equation.

A $8 + x = 14$

SOLUTION

The sum is 14. Subtract 8 from 14 in one subtraction equation, and subtract x from 14 in the other subtraction equation.

$$8 + x = 14$$
$$x = 14 - 8$$
$$8 = 14 - x$$

▶ **Think About It** The equation $14 - 8 = x$ is equivalent to $x = 14 - 8$. The equation $14 - x = 8$ is equivalent to $8 = 14 - x$.

B $21 = 35 - p$

SOLUTION

Because p is subtracted from 35, the sum in the addition equation is 35. Subtract 21 from 35 in the other subtraction equation.

$$p + 21 = 35$$
$$21 = 35 - p$$
$$p = 35 - 21 \ \blacksquare$$

Writing Related Equations for Multiplication and Division

Just like addition and subtraction, multiplication and division are also inverse operations, so you can write related equations using those operations.

Related Equations for Multiplication and Division

For any nonzero a, b, and c,

$$ab = c$$
$$a = \frac{c}{b}$$
$$b = \frac{c}{a}$$

All three are related equations.

Example

$$5 \cdot 2 = 10$$
$$5 = \frac{10}{2}$$
$$2 = \frac{10}{5}$$

All three are related equations.

A good strategy for writing a set of related equations for multiplication and division is to identify the product and write the multiplication equation first. Then, to write the division equations, divide the product by each different factor.

EXAMPLE 2

Write a complete set of related equations for the given equation.

A $4y = 24$

SOLUTION

The product is 24. Divide 24 by 4 in one division equation, and divide 24 by y in the other division equation.

$$4y = 24$$
$$y = 24 \div 4$$
$$4 = 24 \div y$$

> ▶ **Think About It** You can show division with either a division symbol or a fraction. $24 \div 4$ is equivalent to $\frac{24}{4}$.

B $\dfrac{63}{a} = 9$

SOLUTION

Because 63 is divided by a, the product is 63 in the multiplication equation. Divide 63 by 9 in the other division equation.

$$9a = 63$$
$$\dfrac{63}{a} = 9$$
$$\dfrac{63}{9} = a \ \blacksquare$$

Using Related Equations to Solve an Equation

When you find a related equation that has the variable alone on one side of the equation, you can simplify to find the solution.

EXAMPLE 3

Solve using a related equation.

A $9 + x = 12$

SOLUTION

$9 + x = 12$	Use a related equation that has the variable alone on one side of the equation.
$x = 12 - 9$	Subtract.
$x = 3$	

B $7y = 28$

SOLUTION

$7y = 28$	Use a related equation that has the variable alone on one side of the equation.
$y = \dfrac{28}{7}$	Divide.
$y = 4 \ \blacksquare$	

Solving Problems

Problems are easier to solve when you have a plan.

Problem-Solving Plan

Step 1 *Identify* Read the problem and identify the unknowns. What is given? What are you being asked to find? Write it down in words. If you can, estimate the answer.

Step 2 *Strategize* Select and define variables and variable expressions for all the unknowns.

Step 3 *Set Up* Write an equation, inequality, system of equations, or whatever other tools you need that model the problem that is being solved.

Step 4 *Solve* Solve the model (equation, inequality, system, and so on). Answer the question.

Step 5 *Check* Check your answer for reasonableness and accuracy with the original problem statement.

Application: Transportation

EXAMPLE 1

Three times as many cars as trucks went over a bridge. Nineteen trucks went over the bridge. How many vehicles in all went over the bridge?

SOLUTION

Use the problem-solving plan.

Step 1 *Identify*

Given The number of cars is 3 times the number of trucks.
There were 19 trucks.

Need to find total number of vehicles

Step 2 *Strategize* Let $t =$ number of trucks. Then the number of cars $= 3t$.

> ▶ **Think About It** You can solve the problem without using a variable, because the number of trucks is known. But writing variables and variable expressions is a useful skill.

Step 3 *Set Up*

cars $+$ trucks $= 3t + t$ Write an expression for the sum of the numbers of cars and trucks.

Step 4 *Solve*

$3t + t = 3 \cdot 19 + 19$ Substitute 19 for t.

$= 57 + 19$ Simplify.

$= 76$

Seventy-six vehicles went over the bridge.

Step 5 *Check* Estimate to check for reasonableness. There were about 20 trucks. There were about $3 \cdot 20$, or 60 cars: $20 + 60 = 80$, which is close to 76. The answer is reasonable. ■

Application: Geometry

EXAMPLE 2

A A playground is shaped like a square. Each side is 78 ft long. How many times did Maria run around the entire border of the playground if she ran 4992 ft?

SOLUTION

Use the problem-solving plan.

Step 1 *Identify*

Given The playground is square, and each side is 78 ft long. Maria ran 4992 ft.

Need to find how many times Maria ran around the border

Step 2 *Strategize* Let $n =$ the number of times Maria ran around the border.

Step 3 *Set Up*

$4 \cdot 78 = 312$ All four sides of a square have equal length.

$312n = 4992$ Write an equation.

Step 4 *Solve*

$n = \dfrac{4992}{312}$ Use a related equation to solve for n.

$= 16$

Maria ran around the entire border 16 times.

Step 5 *Check* The distance around the playground is about 300 ft. Since $300 \cdot 16 = 4800$, the answer is reasonable.

B What are the possible lengths of a rectangle if the length must be 10 in. longer than the width and the area must be less than 35 in²? Use only whole numbers for the dimensions.

> ▶ **Remember** The area of a rectangle is the product of its length and width.

SOLUTION

Use the problem-solving plan.

Step 1 Identify

Given $length = width + 10$; $area < 35$

Need to find possible lengths for the longer side of the rectangle

Step 2 Strategize Let $w = $ width. Then $length = w + 10$.

Step 3 Set Up Area < 35, so length $\bullet$ width < 35.

$$(w + 10) \bullet w < 35$$

Step 4 Solve Substitute whole numbers for w, starting with 1.

$(w + 10) \bullet w < 35$	$(w + 10) \bullet w < 35$	$(w + 10) \bullet w < 35$
$(1 + 10) \bullet 1 \overset{?}{<} 35$	$(2 + 10) \bullet 2 \overset{?}{<} 35$	$(3 + 10) \bullet 3 \overset{?}{<} 35$
$11 < 35$ ✓	$24 < 35$ ✓	$39 \not< 35$

The possible lengths are $1 + 10$ and $2 + 10$, or 11 in. and 12 in.

Step 5 Check Using a length of 11 in., the dimensions are 1 in. by 11 in. Using a length of 12 in., the dimensions are 2 in. by 12 in. In each case, the length is 10 in. greater than the width and the area is less than 35 in². The answers are reasonable. ▪

Decimals and Problem Solving

The problem-solving plan can make it easier to solve any real-world problem, including problems with decimals.

Identify what you are being asked to solve. Strategize by defining variables and expressions. Once you have defined the variables, set up the problem and solve. Finally check your answer for reasonableness and accuracy.

Problem Solving with Addition and Subtraction

EXAMPLE 1

Each sports team at Carver Middle School had two fund-raisers during the year. The table shows how much money each team raised at each fund-raiser.

Fund-raiser	Soccer team	Baseball team	Basketball team
T-shirts	$125.00	$225.50	$158.50
Candy bars	$75.50	$135.00	$202.25

A How much more money did the soccer team raise at the T-shirt fund-raiser than at the candy bar fund-raiser?

SOLUTION

Use the problem-solving plan.

Step 1 *Identify*

Given The soccer team raised $125.00 at the T-shirt fund-raiser and $75.50 at the candy bar fund-raiser.

Need to find how much more money was raised at T-shirt fund-raiser than at candy bar fund-raiser

Step 2 *Strategize* Let $m =$ how much more money was raised at T-shirt fund-raiser than at candy bar fund-raiser.

Step 3 *Set Up*

$125.00 - 75.50 = m$ The T-shirt fund-raiser raised more money than the candy bar fund-raiser, so subtract $75.50 from $125.00.

Step 4 *Solve*

$125.00 - 75.50 = m$

$49.50 = m$ Subtract.

The soccer team made $49.50 more at the T-shirt fund-raiser than at the candy bar fund-raiser.

Step 5 *Check* Estimate to check for reasonableness. The soccer team raised about $130.00 at the T-shirt fund-raiser and about $80.00 at the candy bar fund-raiser. Since $130.00 - 80.00 = 50.00$, which is close to 49.50, the answer is reasonable.

B What is the total amount the Carver Middle School basketball team raised from the two fund-raisers?

SOLUTION

Use the problem-solving plan.

Step 1 *Identify*

Given The basketball team raised $158.50 at the T-shirt fund-raiser and $202.25 at the candy bar fund-raiser.

Need to find the total amount of money the basketball team raised

Step 2 *Strategize* Let $t =$ the total amount the basketball team raised.

▶ **Remember** A total can be found by using addition.

Step 3 *Set Up*

$158.50 + 202.25 = t$ Add the two given amounts to find the total, t.

Step 4 *Solve*

$158.50 + 202.25 = t$

$\qquad 360.75 = t$ Add.

The basketball team made a total of $360.75 from the two fund-raisers.

Step 5 *Check* Estimate to check for reasonableness. The basketball team raised about $160.00 at the T-shirt fund-raiser and about $200.00 at the candy bar fund-raiser. Since $160.00 + 200.00 = 360.00$, which is close to 360.75, the answer is reasonable. ▪

Problem Solving with Multiplication

EXAMPLE 2

Rectangle A has a length of 6.67 cm and a width of 7.5 cm. Rectangle B has a length of 7.4 cm and a width of 6.72 cm. Which rectangle has the greater area?

SOLUTION

Use the problem-solving plan.

Step 1 *Identify*

Given Rectangle A has a length of 6.67 cm and a width 7.5 cm. Rectangle B has a length of 7.4 cm and a width of 6.72 cm.

Need to find the rectangle with the greater area

Step 2 *Strategize* Let $A =$ the area of Rectangle A. Let $B =$ the area of Rectangle B.

▶ **Remember** The area of a rectangle is $Area = l \cdot w$.

Step 3 *Set Up*

area of Rectangle A: area of Rectangle B:

$A = l \cdot w$ $B - l \cdot w$

Step 4 *Solve*

$A = l \cdot w$ $B - l \cdot w$

$A = 6.67 \cdot 7.5$ $B = 7.4 \cdot 6.72$ Substitute the given values for l and w for each rectangle.

$A - 50.025$ $B = 49.728$ Multiply.

The area of Rectangle A is 50.025 cm^2, and the area of Rectangle B is 49.728 cm^2. Since $50.025 > 49.728$, Rectangle A has the greater area.

Step 5 *Check* Estimate to check for reasonableness. The area of Rectangle A is about $7 \cdot 8 = 56$, or 56 cm^2. The area of Rectangle B is about $7 \cdot 7 = 49$, or 49 cm^2. The estimated area of Rectangle A is greater than the estimated area of Rectangle B. The answer is reasonable. ■

Problem Solving with Division

EXAMPLE 3

A car traveling from one city to another has traveled 282.1 mi in 6.2 h. What is the average speed of the car?

SOLUTION

Use the problem-solving plan.

Step 1 *Identify*

Given The car has traveled 282.1 mi in 6.2 h.

Need to find the average speed of the car

Step 2 *Strategize* Let $s =$ the average speed.

Step 3 *Set Up*

$$s = \frac{\text{total distance}}{\text{elapsed time}}$$

Step 4 *Solve*

$s = \dfrac{282.1}{6.2}$ \quad Substitute the given values for total distance and elapsed time.

$s = 45.5$ \quad Divide.

The average speed of the car is 45.5 mph.

Step 5 *Check* The speed of the car is 45.5 mph. Since $45.5 \cdot 6.2 = 282.1$, the answer is reasonable. ▪

Interpreting Expressions

To solve many problems, you must translate word phrases into variable expressions, equations, or inequalities. There are usually many ways to model any problem.

Working with Multiple Representations

EXAMPLE 1

Ilya sold 10 veggie burgers on Tuesday. On Wednesday, she sold w veggie burgers. On Thursday, Ilya sold t veggie burgers. Each veggie burger sold for $5.

Both the expressions $5(10 + w + t)$ and $50 + 5t + 5w$ represent combined sales, in dollars, of veggie burgers for all 3 days. Explain how each expression represents the combined sales.

> ▶ **Remember** You can use the distributive property in some situations to rewrite an expression. Look for a factor common to all terms in the expression.

SOLUTION

Add the number of veggie burgers sold on the 3 days to get the total number of veggie burgers sold.

$$10 + w + t$$

Multiply the total number sold by the price per veggie burger to get the combined sales.

$$5(10 + w + t)$$

Each veggie burger sells for $5 so total sales on Tuesday, Wednesday, and Thursday were 50, $5w$, and $5t$ dollars. Add these amounts to get the combined sales for all three days.

$$50 + 5w + 5t \blacksquare$$

Modeling Word Problems

EXAMPLE 2

A water tank has 25 gal of water. Water begins to flow from a pipe into the tank at a rate of 6 gal/min. At the same time, water begins to drain from the bottom of the tank at a rate of 2 gal/min. The expression $25 + 4m$ represents the amount of water in the tank, in gallons, after m minutes. Explain how the expression represents this amount.

SOLUTION

Find the amount of water that enters the tank from the pipe.

$$6m.$$

Find the amount of water that drains from the tank.

$$2m.$$

Subtract the amount that drains from the amount of water that enters.

$$6m - 2m$$

Add this amount to the initial amount of water in the tank.

$$25 + 6m - 2m$$

Simplify.

$$25 + 6m - 2m = 25 + 4m \blacksquare$$

▶ **Think About It** What flow rate into the tank would cause the amount of water in the tank to be constant?

Adding and Subtracting Rational Numbers

Topic List

Stock prices rise and fall all day long. These changes are important to investors and to investment firms. Each rise or fall can be understood in terms of subtraction, with the hope that the end result adds to the investors' or the companies' bottom line.

Integers on a Number Line

A number line goes in two directions. To the right of zero are positive numbers. To the left of zero are negative numbers.

Nonzero opposites are two numbers that are the same distance from zero on a number line. A **number line** can be used to compare and order numbers. Every number has its own corresponding point on a number line.

The set of **integers** is {. . ., −3, −2, −1, 0, 1, 2, 3, . . .}. It is the set of whole numbers and their opposites.

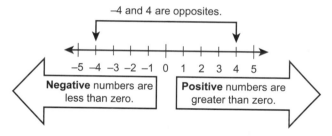

The opposite of zero is zero. Zero is neither positive nor negative.

▶ **Think About It** Zero is a whole number and an integer.

Identifying Coordinates of Points on a Number Line

A **coordinate** is a number that indicates the location of a point on a number line. The **origin** is the point on a number line with coordinate 0.

EXAMPLE 1

State the coordinate of each indicated point on the number line.

A point *A*

SOLUTION

Point *A* is the origin. The coordinate of point *A* is 0.

B point *B*

SOLUTION

Point *B* is 3 units to the right of the origin. The coordinate of point *B* is 3.

▶ **Think About It** A number with no symbol in front is positive, so 3 represents positive 3, which can also be represented as +3 .

C point *C*

SOLUTION

Point *C* is 4 units to the left of the origin. The coordinate of point *C* is −4.

D point *D*

SOLUTION

Point *D* is 7 units to the left of the origin. The coordinate of point *D* is −7. ▪

Graphing Integers on a Number Line

To graph an integer on a number line, begin at the origin, and then count the correct number of units right or left. Draw a dot to represent the point and label the point with its coordinate.

▶ **Think About It** A point is the graph, or plot, of a number. A number is the coordinate of a point.

EXAMPLE 2

Graph the number on a number line.

A 6

SOLUTION

Since 6 is positive, it is to the right of the origin. Start at zero and count
6 units to the right.

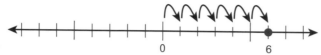

B −3

SOLUTION

Since −3 is negative, it is to the left of the origin. Start at zero and count
3 units to the left.

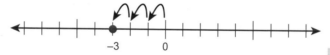

Comparing Numbers

Graphing numbers on a number line can help you compare them. Numbers
increase in value as you move to the right. Numbers decrease in value as you
move to the left. So, when comparing two numbers, the number to the left is
less and the number to the right is greater.

EXAMPLE 3

Use a number line to compare the integers. Use $<$, $>$, or $=$.

A 2 and −4

SOLUTION

Because −4 is to the left of 2, you know that −4 is less than 2. So you can
write either $-4 < 2$ or $2 > -4$.

> ▶ **Remember** The inequalities −4 < 2 and 2 > −4 are equivalent. You can say negative four is less than two or two is greater than negative four.

B −6 and −2

SOLUTION

Because −6 is to the left of −2, you know that −6 is less than −2. So you can write either −6 < −2 or −2 > −6. ■

Absolute Value

The **absolute value** of a number is its distance from zero. Absolute value is indicated by the | | symbol. For example, read |−4| as "the absolute value of negative four."

EXAMPLE 4

A Find |−4|.

SOLUTION

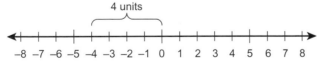

Since −4 is 4 units from zero, |−4| = 4.

B Find |6|.

SOLUTION

Since 6 is 6 units from zero, |6| = 6. ■

Opposite Numbers

Numbers are opposites if they are the same distance from zero but in different directions on a number line. Another property of opposites is that they have different signs (except for zero) but the same absolute value. For example, 12 and -12 are opposites because they have different signs, but $|12| = 12$ and $|-12| = 12$.

▶ **Think About It** The same sign is used for opposite, negative, and subtraction.

The $-$ sign is used to indicate opposite. You can read -2 as either "negative two" or "the opposite of two." Read $-(-2)$ as "the opposite of negative two." The opposite of -2 is 2, so write $-(-2) = 2$ and read it as "the opposite of negative two equals two."

EXAMPLE 5

Write the opposite of the integer.

A 3

SOLUTION
The opposite of 3 is -3.

B -10

SOLUTION
The opposite of -10 is 10, or $-(-10) = 10$.

C 0

SOLUTION
The opposite of 0 is 0. ■

▶ **Think About It** All numbers have opposites, not just integers. For example, the opposite of 3.4 is -3.4.

Identifying Integer Solutions of Absolute Value Open Sentences

You can use a number line to help identify integer solutions of simple equations and inequalities involving absolute value.

> **Remember** An open sentence is an equation or inequality that contains one or more variables. A solution of an open sentence is a number that makes it true.

EXAMPLE 6

Identify all integer solutions of the equation or inequality.

A $|x| = 7$

SOLUTION

The absolute value of x is 7, so all values of x are 7 units from zero on a number line.

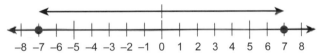

The integer solutions of $|x| = 7$ are -7 and 7.

B $|x| < 3$

SOLUTION

The absolute value of x is less than 3, so all values of x are less than 3 units from zero on a number line.

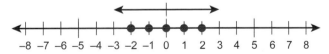

The integer solutions of $|x| < 3$ are -2, -1, 0, 1, and 2. ∎

> **Think About It** There are many solutions of $|x| < 3$ that are not integers. Two solutions are -1.55 and $2\frac{3}{4}$.

Application: Weather

EXAMPLE 7

The table shows the temperatures for five cities on a particular day. Plot the temperatures on a number line. Then list the cities in order from coldest to warmest.

City	Temperature (°C)
Ottawa, Canada	−6
Los Angeles, CA	11
Seward, AK	−7
Houston, TX	6
Washington, DC	−1

SOLUTION

The cities from coldest to warmest are Seward, Ottawa, Washington, Houston, and Los Angeles. ■

Additive Inverses

If the sum of two quantities is zero, the quantities are additive inverses.

Finding an Additive Inverse on a Number Line

Additive Inverse Property

The sum of a number a and its additive inverse $-a$ is 0.

You can use a number line to represent additive inverses.

▶ **Remember** The additive inverse of a number is its opposite. For example, the additive inverse of -4 is $-(-4)$, or 4.

EXAMPLE 1

Yuna started a hike at sea level. She climbed to the top of a hill, at an altitude of 281 m. She descended the same route and finished her hike at sea level. How many meters in altitude did Yuna descend? Draw a number line to represent the situation. Explain your reasoning.

▶ **Remember** A number and its additive inverse have the same absolute value.

SOLUTION

Yuna ascended from sea level, which is 0 m, to 281 m above sea level. To represent her climb, start at 0 and move 281 units to the right on the number line. Since the sum of her gain in altitude and loss in altitude equals 0, the number that represents Yuna's descent must be the additive inverse of the number for her climb. To represent her descent on the number line, begin at 281 and move 281 units to the left, or -281 units.

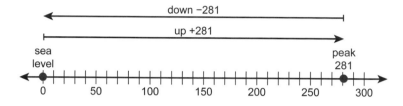

CHECK

$$281 + (-281) = 0 \checkmark \;\blacksquare$$

EXAMPLE 2

In an American football game, a team loses 3 yd on first down. The team loses another 7 yd on second down.

> ▶ **Think About It** In American football, a down is an attempt to move the ball forward. A team has 4 downs to move the ball forward a total of 10 yd.

A How many yards must the team gain on third down so that the overall change in yardage is 0? Show your reasoning using a number line.

SOLUTION

A loss of 3 yd on first down is represented by moving 3 units to the left from 0. A loss of 7 yd on second down is represented by moving 7 units to the left from -3, leading to a total loss of 10 yd. This change is represented by the point -10 on the number line.

To end third down with no net change in yardage, the team must gain yardage to end up at zero. This change is represented by moving 10 units to the right from -10, ending up on 0.

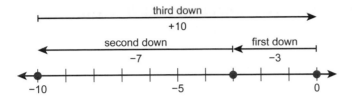

▶ **Think About It** Can you think of other real-world situations in which the end result is an overall, or net, change of 0?

B Suppose that the overall change in yardage after 4 downs is 0 and that the team gained the same number of yards on both third and fourth downs. How many yards did the team gain on each of third and fourth downs? Show your reasoning using a number line.

SOLUTION
The team lost a total of 10 yd after first and second downs. To finish with 0 overall change in yardage, the team must have gained a total of 10 yd on third and fourth downs.

The 10 yd is divided evenly between third and fourth downs, so the team gained 5 yd on each down. This calculation is represented by moving 5 units to the right twice on the number line, ending up on 0.

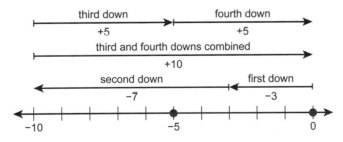

CHECK

$$-10 + 5 + 5 = 0 \checkmark \ \blacksquare$$

Absolute Value and Distance

The distance between two different points is always a positive number. It doesn't matter whether you measure from point A to point B or from point B to point A; the distance is always positive.

Equidistant Points Occur in Pairs

For any two points with coordinates p and $p + q$, the distance between the two points is $|q|$. When you plot point p and try to plot a point that is q units away from p, there are two possibilities. Either q is negative (so the second point is to the left of p) or q is positive (the second point is to the right of p).

EXAMPLE 1

Frank climbed up a ladder to wash a window. At first, he climbed 7 rungs up the ladder. Then he changed his position on the ladder. His new position is 2 rungs away from his previous position.

▶ **Remember** The absolute value of a number can never be negative.

A The two expressions represent Frank's possible positions on the ladder now. Represent each on a number line.

$$7 + 2$$
$$7 - 2$$

SOLUTION

A vertical number line usually has positive numbers increasing upward just as a horizontal number line increases to the right.

For these expressions, start at 0 and go up to 7 for the first addend. Then go up for the addend $+2$ and down for -2.

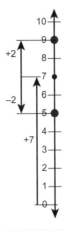

▶ ## Q&A

Q Suppose Frank's third position is 4 rungs away from his second position. How many rungs up the ladder could Frank be?

A Four possibilities exist.

$$7 + 2 + 4 = 13$$
$$7 + 2 - 4 = 5$$
$$7 - 2 + 4 = 9$$
$$7 - 2 - 4 = 1$$

B Explain how each expression in Example 1A represents traveling a distance of 2 rungs from Frank's previous position.

SOLUTION

The expression $7 + 2$ represents going up 7 rungs and then going up 2 more rungs. Frank travels in the same direction (up) both times.

The expression $7 - 2$ represents Frank going up 7 rungs and then going in the opposite direction (down) 2 rungs.

Since $|2| = 2$ and $|-2| = 2$, both cases represent traveling a distance of 2 rungs from the previous position. ■

EXAMPLE 2

Sadie drove 35 mi due west from her home along an east-west highway to visit her grandmother. After the visit, Sadie wanted to eat lunch. Sadie's GPS showed that a restaurant was 8 mi away along the same highway.

▶ **Think About It** A global positioning system (GPS) is an electronic device that tells you your location on the earth by determining your distance from three or more satellites (and by using some fancy math).

A Write two expressions that represent the possible positions of the restaurant from Sadie's home along the highway. Represent the two expressions on a number line.

SOLUTION

Two expressions to represent the situation are $-35 + 8$ and $-35 - 8$.

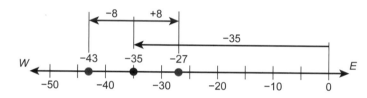

B Explain how each expression in Example 2A represents the same distance from Sadie's grandmother's house.

SOLUTION

The expression $-35 + 8$ represents going 35 mi west and then going in the opposite direction, 8 mi east, to reach the restaurant.

The expression $-35 - 8$ represents going 35 mi west and then going another 8 mi west to reach the restaurant.

Since $|8| = 8$ and $|-8| = 8$, both cases represent Sadie traveling a distance of 8 mi from her grandmother's house, though the two trips are in opposite directions. ∎

Adding Integers

You can use a number line to add integers.

How to Use a Number Line to Add Integers

Start at 0.

For positive integers, move right; for negative integers, move left.

The ending point of each move is the starting point for the next move.
The ending point of the last move is the answer.

▶ **Think About It** In any addition expression, the numbers being added are called addends.

Using a Number Line to Add Integers

EXAMPLE 1

Use a number line to find the sum.

A $3 + (-7)$

SOLUTION

Start at 0. Move 3 units right. From 3, move 7 units left.

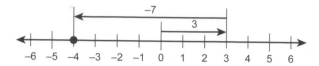

$3 + (-7) = -4$

> ▶ **Think About It** You can start with either integer.
> $$3 + (-7) = -7 + 3$$

B $-4 + (-2)$

SOLUTION

Start at 0. Move 4 units left. From -4, move 2 units left.

$-4 + (-2) = -6$ ▪

Using Rules to Add Integers

In addition to a number line, you can also use rules to add integers.

Rules for Adding Two Integers

If the signs are the same, add the absolute values of the integers. The sum has the same sign as the addends.

If the signs are different, find the difference of the absolute values. The sum has the same sign as the addend with the greater absolute value.

EXAMPLE 2

Find the sum.

A $-20 + (-13)$

SOLUTION

Both addends are negative. The sum will be negative.

$$-20 + (-13) = -(|-20| + |-13|) \qquad \text{The sum is negative.}$$
$$= -(20 + 13) \qquad \text{Evaluate the absolute values.}$$
$$= -33 \qquad \text{Add.}$$

> **Remember** Absolute value is always nonnegative.
> $$|-25| = 25$$
> $$|35| = 35$$

B $-25 + 35$

SOLUTION

The addends have different signs. Because $|35|$ is greater than $|-25|$, the sum will be positive.

$$-25 + 35 = +(|35| - |-25|) \qquad \text{The sum is positive.}$$
$$= 35 - 25 \qquad \text{Evaluate the absolute values.}$$
$$= 10 \qquad \text{Subtract.}$$

CHECK

Use a number line.

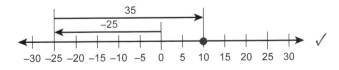

The sum is 10.

Evaluating Expressions

Evaluate variable expressions by substituting values for the variables and then simplifying.

EXAMPLE 3

A Evaluate $a + b$ when $a = 5$ and $b = -1$.

SOLUTION

$a + b = 5 + (-1)$ Substitute 5 for a and -1 for b.

$\qquad = 4$ Add.

B Evaluate $x + y + z$ when $x = -43$, $y = -17$, and $z = -10$.

SOLUTION

$x + y + z = -43 + (-17) + (-10)$ Substitute -43 for x, -17 for y, and -10 for z.

$\qquad = -60 + (-10)$ Add from left to right.

$\qquad = -70$ ◼

Comparing Expressions

EXAMPLE 4

Select the symbol ($<$, $>$, or $=$) that makes a true statement.

A $3 + (-4) \blacksquare 5 + (-2)$

SOLUTION

$3 + (-4) \blacksquare 5 + (-2)$ Evaluate the expression on each side.

$\quad -1 \quad < \quad 3$ Since -1 is less than 3, use the $<$ symbol.

$3 + (-4) < 5 + (-2)$

B $8 + (-20) \blacksquare -7 + (-10)$

SOLUTION

$8 + (-20)$ ■ $-7 + (-10)$ Evaluate the expression on each side.

$-12 \quad > \quad -17$ Since -12 is greater than -17, use the $>$ symbol.

$8 + (-20) > -7 + (-10)$

> **Think About It** To compare -12 and -17, plot them on a number line. The lesser number is on the left and the greater number is on the right.

C $-3 + 8 + (-11)$ ■ $10 + (-16)$

SOLUTION

$-3 + 8 + (-11)$ ■ $10 + (-16)$ Evaluate the expression on each side.

$-6 \quad = \quad -6$ Since -6 is equal to -6, use the $=$ symbol.

$-3 + 8 + (-11) = 10 + (-16)$ ■

Addition Properties

Here are two useful properties for addition.

Addition Properties	
Property	**Example**
Identity Property for Addition The sum of any number and zero is equal to the number. Zero is called the **additive identity**.	
$a + 0 = a$ $0 + a = a$	$-5 + 0 = -5$ $0 + 8 = 8$
Property of Inverses for Addition The sum of any number and its opposite is equal to zero. Opposites are also called additive inverses.	
$a + (-a) = 0$ $-a + a = 0$	$3 + (-3) = 0$ $-10 + 10 = 0$ $-7 + (-(-7)) = 0$

EXAMPLE 5

Find the value of the variable that makes the statement true.

A $x + 5 = 0$

SOLUTION

The property of inverses for addition states that the sum of any number and its opposite is 0. Because the sum is 0, you know that x is the opposite of 5. So $x = -5$.

B $-4 + x = -4$

SOLUTION

The identity property for addition states that the sum of any number and 0 is equal to the same number. Because -4 plus x is equal to -4, you know that x is 0. So $x = 0$. ▪

Application: Banking

EXAMPLE 6

The table shows deposits and withdrawals in a new bank account that is opened with the deposit on Monday. How much is in the account at the end of the week?

Day	Deposit or withdrawal ($)
Monday	+50
Wednesday	−27
Thursday	+30
Friday	−13

SOLUTION

$$50 + (-27) + 30 + (-13) = 23 + 30 + (-13)$$
$$= 53 + (-13)$$
$$= 40$$

At the end of the week, the account contains $40. ▪

Adding Decimals and Fractions

Adding decimals and fractions on a number line is similar to adding integers.

Using a Number Line to Add Decimals

As with integers, a negative decimal can be shown with a line segment pointing to the left, while a positive decimal can be shown with a segment pointing to the right.

EXAMPLE 1

Find the sum.

A $-1.6 + (-0.8)$

SOLUTION
Start at 0. Move 1.6 units left. From -1.6, move 0.8 unit left.

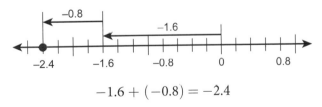

$$-1.6 + (-0.8) = -2.4$$

B $0.5 + (-1.8)$

SOLUTION

Start at 0. Move 0.5 unit right. From 0.5, move 1.8 units left.

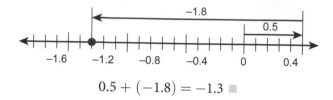

$$0.5 + (-1.8) = -1.3 \; \blacksquare$$

> ▶ **Remember** Check the scale of the number line you are using. The distance between tick marks in Example 1A is 0.2. The distance between tick marks in Example 1B is 0.1.

Using a Number Line to Add Fractions

You can use a number line to add positive and negative fractions.

EXAMPLE 2

Find the sum.

A $-\dfrac{1}{3} + \left(-\dfrac{2}{4}\right)$

SOLUTION

Step 1 Rewrite the fractions using the least common denominator.

$$-\frac{1}{3} \cdot \frac{4}{4} + \left(-\frac{2}{4} \cdot \frac{3}{3}\right) = -\frac{4}{12} + \left(-\frac{6}{12}\right)$$

> ▶ **Think About It** The least common denominator is 12. Multiply each addend by a fraction that is a form of 1 to get an equivalent fraction with a denominator of 12.

Step 2 Start at 0. Move $\frac{4}{12}$ unit to the left. From $-\frac{4}{12}$, move $\frac{6}{12}$ unit left.

$$-\frac{1}{3} + \left(-\frac{2}{4}\right) = -\frac{10}{12} = -\frac{5}{6}$$

▶ **Remember** Just like integers, negative fractions are shown with an arrow pointing to the left, and positive fractions are shown with an arrow pointing to the right.

B $1\frac{4}{5} + \left(-\frac{1}{2}\right)$

SOLUTION

Step 1 Write the mixed number as an improper fraction.

$$1\frac{4}{5} + \left(-\frac{1}{2}\right) = \frac{9}{5} + \left(-\frac{1}{2}\right)$$

Step 2 Rewrite the fractions using the least common denominator.

$$\frac{9}{5} \cdot \frac{2}{2} + \left(-\frac{1}{2} \cdot \frac{5}{5}\right) = \frac{18}{10} + \left(-\frac{5}{10}\right)$$

Step 3 Start at 0. Move $\frac{18}{10}$ units to the right. From $\frac{18}{10}$, move $\frac{5}{10}$ unit left.

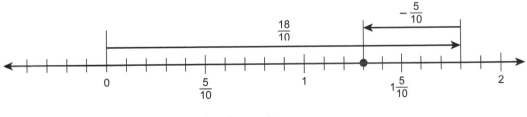

$$1\frac{4}{5} + \left(-\frac{1}{2}\right) = 1\frac{3}{10}$$ ▪

Using Rules to Add Decimals and Fractions

The rules for adding positive and negative decimals are the same as the rules for adding positive and negative integers.

Rules for Adding Two Decimals

If the signs are the same, add the absolute values of the decimals. Use the same sign as the decimals.

If the signs are different, find the difference of the absolute values. Use the sign of the decimal with the greater absolute value.

EXAMPLE 3

Find the sum.

A $-6.7 + (-1.3)$

SOLUTION
Both signs are negative. The answer will be negative.

$$-6.7 + (-1.3) = -|-6.7| + |-1.3| \qquad \text{Add the absolute values.}$$
$$= -(6.7 + 1.3)$$
$$= -8.0 \qquad \text{The sum has the same sign as the addends.}$$

B $-27.8 + 14.3$

SOLUTION
The signs are different. Because $|-27.8|$ is greater than $|14.3|$, the answer will be negative.

$$-27.8 + 14.3 = -(|-27.8| - |14.3|) \qquad \text{Subtract the smaller absolute value from the greater}$$
$$= -(27.8 - 14.3) \qquad \text{absolute value. The sum has the sign of the decimal}$$
$$= -13.5 \ \blacksquare \qquad \text{with the greater absolute value.}$$

EXAMPLE 4

Find the sum.

A $-\frac{1}{6} + \left(-\frac{2}{3}\right)$

SOLUTION

Both addends are negative. The sum will be negative.

$$-\frac{1}{6} + \left(-\frac{2}{3}\right) = -\left(\left|-\frac{1}{6}\right| + \left|-\frac{2}{3}\right|\right) \qquad \text{The sum is negative.}$$

$$= -\left(\frac{1}{6} + \frac{2}{3}\right) \qquad \text{Evaluate the absolute values.}$$

$$= -\left(\frac{1}{6} + \frac{4}{6}\right) \qquad \text{Rewrite the fractions using the least common denominator.}$$

$$= -\frac{5}{6} \qquad \text{Add.}$$

$$-\frac{1}{6} + \left(-\frac{2}{3}\right) = -\frac{5}{6}$$

B $\frac{1}{3} + \left(-\frac{6}{7}\right)$

▶ **Remember** If the signs are different, find the difference of the absolute values. Subtract the smaller absolute value from the greater absolute value. The sum has the same sign as the addend with the greater absolute value.

SOLUTION

The addends have different signs. Because $\left|-\frac{6}{7}\right|$ is greater than $\left|\frac{1}{3}\right|$, the sum will be negative.

$$\frac{1}{3} + \left(-\frac{6}{7}\right) = -\left(\left|-\frac{6}{7}\right| - \left|\frac{1}{3}\right|\right) \qquad \text{The sum is negative.}$$

$$= -\left(\frac{6}{7} - \frac{1}{3}\right) \qquad \text{Evaluate the absolute values.}$$

$$= -\left(\frac{18}{21} - \frac{7}{21}\right) \qquad \text{Rewrite the fractions using the least common denominator.}$$

$$= -\frac{11}{21} \qquad \text{Subtract.}$$

$$\frac{1}{3} + \left(-\frac{6}{7}\right) = -\frac{11}{21} \ \blacksquare$$

Evaluating Expressions with Decimals

Evaluate variable expressions by substituting values for the variables.

EXAMPLE 5

A Evaluate $a + b$ when $a = 1.5$ and $b = -2.8$.

SOLUTION

$a + b = \mathbf{1.5} + (\mathbf{-2.8})$ Substitute 1.5 for a and -2.8 for b. Subtract absolute values.

$= -1.3$ Use the sign of the greater absolute value.

B Evaluate $-0.6 + r + z$ when $r = -5.09$ and $z = -1.2$.

SOLUTION

$-0.6 + r + z = -0.6 + (\mathbf{-5.09}) + (\mathbf{-1.2})$ Substitute -5.09 for r and -1.2 for z.

$= -6.89$ Add absolute values.

The sum is -6.89.

C Evaluate $c + d + f$ when $c = -2.2$, $d = -5.1$, and $f = 10.5$.

SOLUTION

$$c + d + f = -2.2 + (-5.1) + 10.5 \qquad \text{Substitute } -2.2 \text{ for } c, -5.1 \text{ for } d, \text{ and } 10.5 \text{ for } f.$$

$$= -7.3 + 10.5 \qquad \text{Add from left to right.}$$

$$= 3.2 \ \blacksquare$$

Using Related Equations to Solve Subtraction Equations

You can use related equations to solve subtraction equations. Just find a related equation with the variable alone on one side of the equation.

EXAMPLE 6

Solve the equation.

A $x - 3.2 = 6.04$

SOLUTION

$$x - 3.2 = 6.04 \qquad \text{Write the given subtraction equation.}$$

$$x = 3.2 + 6.04 \qquad \text{Write the related addition equation.}$$

$$x = 9.24 \qquad \text{Add.}$$

> ▶ **Remember** To add decimals, align the decimal points. Write zeros as placeholders if needed. Use the correct rule regarding positive and negative signs.

B $n - (-0.9) = 1.25$

SOLUTION

$$n - (-0.9) = 1.25 \qquad \text{Write the given subtraction equation.}$$

$$n = -0.9 + 1.25 \qquad \text{Write the related addition equation.}$$

$$n = 0.35 \qquad \text{Add.} \ \blacksquare$$

Application: Animals

EXAMPLE 7

Jess is tracking the movement of a garden snail toward a plant. The table shows the snail's progress each minute. A positive number indicates movement forward. A negative number indicates movement backward. What is the net forward progress of the snail toward the plant?

Minute	Distance traveled (in.)
1	$+1.9$
2	-0.5
3	$+2.3$
4	$+1.1$

SOLUTION

The net forward progress is the sum of the positive and negative numbers.

$$1.9 + (-0.5) + 2.3 + 1.1 = 1.4 + 2.3 + 1.1 \qquad \text{Add from left to right.}$$
$$= 3.7 + 1.1$$
$$= 4.8$$

The net forward progress of the snail toward the plant is 4.8 in. ■

Subtracting Integers

In simple arithmetic, subtraction is the same as taking away. In algebra, subtraction is the same as adding the opposite.

To subtract an integer, you add its opposite.

Subtracting Integers	
Property	**Example**
Subtracting an integer is the same as adding its opposite.	
$a - b = a + (-b)$ $a - (-b) = a + b$	$1 - 5 = 1 + (-5)$ $10 - (-4) = 10 + 4$

Subtracting Integers

EXAMPLE 1

Find the difference.

A $2 - 7$

SOLUTION

$2 - 7 = 2 + (-7)$ Rewrite as adding the opposite of 7.

$ = -5$

B $3 - (-5)$

SOLUTION

$$3 - (-5) = 3 + 5 \qquad \text{Add the opposite of } -5.$$
$$= 8$$

C $-4 - 11$

SOLUTION

$$-4 - 11 = -4 + (-11) \qquad \text{Add the opposite of } 11.$$
$$= -15$$

D $-47 - (-7)$

SOLUTION

$$-47 - (-7) = -47 + 7 \qquad \text{Add the opposite of } -7.$$
$$= -40 \ \blacksquare$$

▶ **Think About It** The rules for adding and subtracting integers apply to adding and subtracting all real numbers.

$$-3.2 - 4.5 = -3.2 + (-4.5)$$
$$= -7.7$$

Evaluating Expressions

Evaluate variable expressions by substituting values for the variables.

EXAMPLE 2

A Evaluate $a - b$ when $a = -1$ and $b = -6$.

SOLUTION

$$a - b = -1 - (-6) \qquad \text{Substitute } -1 \text{ for } a \text{ and } -6 \text{ for } b.$$
$$= -1 + 6 \qquad \text{Add the opposite of } -6.$$
$$= 5$$

B Evaluate $20 - x - y$ when $x = 14$ and $y = -6$.

SOLUTION

$$\begin{aligned} 20 - x - y &= 20 - \mathbf{14} - (\mathbf{-6}) && \text{Substitute 14 for } x \text{ and } -6 \text{ for } y. \\ &= 20 + (-14) + 6 && \text{Rewrite using addition.} \\ &= 6 + 6 && \text{Add from left to right.} \\ &= 12 \end{aligned}$$

C Evaluate $c - d + f$ when $c = -2$, $d = 18$, and $f = -11$.

SOLUTION

$$\begin{aligned} c - d + f &= \mathbf{-2} - \mathbf{18} + (\mathbf{-11}) && \text{Substitute } -2 \text{ for } c, 18 \text{ for } d, \text{ and } -11 \text{ for } f. \\ &= -2 + (-18) + (-11) && \text{Rewrite using addition.} \\ &= -20 + (-11) && \text{Add from left to right.} \\ &= -31 \ \blacksquare \end{aligned}$$

Application: Geography

EXAMPLE 3

Driskill Mountain, Louisiana, has an elevation of 535 ft. In large portions of the city of New Orleans, the average elevation is −9 ft. What is the difference between those two elevations?

SOLUTION

Subtract the lower elevation from the higher elevation.

$$\begin{aligned} 535 - (-9) &= 535 + 9 \\ &= 544 \end{aligned}$$

The difference between the elevations is 544 ft. ■

Subtracting Decimals and Fractions

Before subtracting decimals and fractions that involve negative numbers, review the procedures for subtracting decimals vertically.

Subtracting Decimals Vertically

Remember to align the decimal points when you subtract, just as you do when you add. Use zeros as placeholders when necessary.

EXAMPLE 1

Find the difference.

A 129.52 − 14.2

SOLUTION

```
  129.52     Align the decimal points.
− 14.20      Write a zero as a placeholder.
  115.32     Subtract.
```

> ▶ **Think About It** You can check your subtraction by adding.
>
> $$\begin{array}{r} 115.32 \\ + 14.20 \\ \hline 129.52 \end{array}$$

B 20.56 − 8.473

SOLUTION

```
  20.560     Align the decimal points. Write a zero as a placeholder.
−  8.473
  12.087     Regroup as needed. Subtract. ■
```

Using a Number Line to Subtract Decimals and Fractions

You can use a number line to subtract decimals and fractions.

EXAMPLE 2

Find the difference.

A $1.25 - 2.75$

SOLUTION
Start at 0. Move 1.25 units to the right. From 1.25, move 2.75 units left.

> ▶ **Remember** When you use a number line to subtract a positive number, you move to the left.

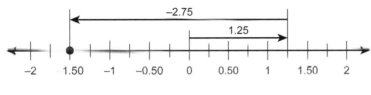

$$1.25 - 2.75 = -1.50$$

B $\frac{1}{2} - \left(-\frac{3}{8} \right)$

SOLUTION
Step 1 Rewrite the fractions using the least common denominator.

$$\frac{1}{2} - \left(-\frac{3}{8} \right) = \frac{4}{8} - \left(-\frac{3}{8} \right)$$

> ▶ **Remember** Subtracting a negative is equivalent to adding a positive.

Step 2 Start at 0. Move $\frac{4}{8}$ unit right. From $\frac{4}{8}$, move $\frac{3}{8}$ unit right.

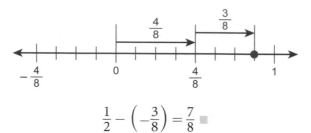

$$\frac{1}{2} - \left(-\frac{3}{8}\right) = \frac{7}{8} \ \blacksquare$$

Using a Rule to Subtract Decimals and Fractions

The rule for subtracting any number, including a decimal or fraction, is the same as the rule for subtracting an integer.

Subtracting a Number
To subtract a number, add its opposite. $$a - b = a + (-b)$$

EXAMPLE 3

Subtract.

A $2.3 - 4.5$

SOLUTION

$$2.3 - 4.5 = 2.3 + (-4.5) \qquad$$ Write subtraction as adding the opposite.

$$= -\left(|-4.5| - |2.3|\right) \qquad$$ The signs of 2.3 and -4.5 are different, so subtract the absolute values. The difference has the sign of the number with the greater absolute value.

$$= -\left(4.5 - 2.3\right)$$

$$= -2.2$$

B $24.3 - (-11.5)$

SOLUTION

$24.3 - (-11.5) = 24.3 + 11.5$ Write subtraction as adding the opposite of -11.5.

                $= 35.8$

C $-0.04 - (-10.1)$

SOLUTION

$-0.04 - (-10.1) = -0.04 + 10.1$ Write subtraction as adding the opposite.

                $= |10.1| - |-0.04|$ The signs of -0.04 and 10.1 are different, so subtract the absolute values.

                $= 10.1 - 0.04$

                $= 10.06$ The difference has the sign of the number with the greater absolute value. ■

EXAMPLE 4

Find the difference.

A $\frac{1}{2} - \left(-\frac{2}{5}\right)$

> ▶ **Remember** To subtract a number, you add its opposite.

SOLUTION

$\frac{1}{2} - \left(-\frac{2}{5}\right) = \frac{1}{2} + \frac{2}{5}$ Rewrite the subtraction as adding the opposite.

            $= \frac{5}{10} + \frac{4}{10}$ Rewrite the fractions using the least common denominator.

            $= \frac{9}{10}$ Add.

$$\frac{1}{2} - \left(-\frac{2}{5}\right) = \frac{9}{10}$$

B $-\frac{1}{3} - \left(-\frac{1}{12}\right)$

SOLUTION

$$-\frac{1}{3} - \left(-\frac{1}{12}\right) = -\frac{1}{3} + \left(\frac{1}{12}\right)$$ Rewrite subtraction as adding the opposite.

$$= -\left(\left|-\frac{1}{3}\right| - \left|\frac{1}{12}\right|\right)$$ The signs of $-\frac{1}{3}$ and $\frac{1}{12}$ are different, so subtract the

absolute values. The difference has the sign of the number with the greater absolute value.

$$= -\left(\frac{4}{12} - \frac{1}{12}\right)$$ Rewrite the fractions using the least common denominator.

$$= -\frac{3}{12}$$ Subtract.

$$-\frac{1}{3} - \left(-\frac{1}{12}\right) = -\frac{3}{12} = -\frac{1}{4} \;\blacksquare$$

Using Related Equations to Solve Addition Equations

Because addition and subtraction are inverse operations, you can solve an addition equation by subtracting. To solve a simple addition equation, write the related subtraction equation that has the variable alone on one side of the equation.

EXAMPLE 5

Solve the equation.

A $r + 7.5 = -3$

SOLUTION

$r + 7.5 = -3$ Write the given addition equation.

$r = -3 - 7.5$ Write the related subtraction equation that has the variable alone on one side of the equation. Then subtract.

$r = -10.5$

B $-2.4 + t = 1.05$

> ▶ **Think About It** For the addition equation $-2.4 + t = 1.05$, the two related subtraction equations are $t = 1.05 - (-2.4)$ and $-2.4 = 1.05 - t$.

SOLUTION

$-2.4 + t = 1.05$	Write the given addition equation.
$t = 1.05 - (-2.4)$	Write the related subtraction equation that has the variable alone on one side of the equation. Then simplify.
$t = 1.05 + 2.4$	
$t - 3.45$	

C $x + (-0.85) = -1$

SOLUTION

$x + (-0.85) = -1$	Write the given addition equation.
$x = -1 - (-0.85)$	Write the related subtraction equation that has the variable alone on one side of the equation. Then simplify.
$x = -1 + 0.85$	
$x = -0.15$ ∎	

Evaluating Expressions with Decimals

EXAMPLE 6

> ▶ **Think About It** For any numbers a and b, $a - b$ and $b - a$ are opposites. Examples 6A and 6B illustrate this property.

A Evaluate $a - b$ when $a = 3.1$ and $b = -4.6$.

SOLUTION

$$a - b = 3.1 - (-4.6) \qquad \text{Substitute 3.1 for } a \text{ and } -4.6 \text{ for } b.$$

$$= 3.1 + 4.6 \qquad \text{Add the opposite of } -4.6.$$

$$= 7.7$$

B Evaluate $b - a$ when $a = 3.1$ and $b = -4.6$.

SOLUTION

$$b - a = -4.6 - 3.1 \qquad \text{Substitute } -4.6 \text{ for } b \text{ and 3.1 for } a.$$

$$= -4.6 + (-3.1) \qquad \text{Add the opposite of 3.1.}$$

$$= -7.7$$

C Evaluate $u - 3.5 - s$ when $u = -4$ and $s = -0.1$.

SOLUTION

$$u - 3.5 - s = -4 - 3.5 - (-0.1) \qquad \text{Substitute } -4 \text{ for } u \text{ and } -0.1 \text{ for } s.$$

$$= -4.0 + (-3.5) + 0.1 \qquad \text{Write } -4 \text{ as } -4.0. \text{ Add the opposite of 3.5 and the}$$
$$\text{opposite of } -0.1. \text{ Add from left to right.}$$

$$= -7.5 + 0.1$$

$$= -7.4 \ \blacksquare$$

Addition and Subtraction Properties

You have already learned some properties of addition. Here are three more useful properties of addition.

Addition Properties	
Property	**Example**
Commutative Property Numbers can be added in any order. $a + b = b + a$	$2 + (-5) = -5 + 2$ $-3 = -3 \checkmark$
Associative Property For three or more numbers, their sum is always the same, no matter how the numbers are grouped. $(a + b) + c = b + (b + c)$	$(-1 + 7) + 4 = -1 + (7 + 4)$ $6 + 4 = -1 + 11$ $10 = 10 \checkmark$
Opposite of a Sum The opposite of the sum of two numbers is equal to the sum of the opposites. $-(a + b) = -a + (-b)$	$-(5 + 3) = -5 + (-3)$ $-8 = -8 \checkmark$

Identifying Addition Properties

Identify the property shown.

A $-3 + 4 = 4 + (-3)$

SOLUTION

The order of the numbers being added is changed. The property shown is the commutative property of addition.

B $5 + (-8 + 10) = (5 + (-8)) + 10$

SOLUTION

The numbers being added are grouped differently. The property shown is the associative property of addition.

C $15 + (-7) + 5 = 15 + 5 + (-7)$

SOLUTION

The order of -7 and 5 is changed. The property shown is the commutative property of addition.

▶ **Think About It** Parentheses do not always indicate the associative property. In Example 1C, parentheses are used to separate negative signs from addition signs.

D $-(-1 + 7) = 1 + (-7)$

SOLUTION

The equation states that the opposite of the sum of -1 and 7 is equal to the sum of 1 and -7. The property shown is the property of the opposite of a sum. ■

Using Addition Properties

Using the associative and commutative properties of addition can make some expressions easier to evaluate with mental math.

EXAMPLE 2

Use properties to rewrite the expression, and then evaluate it.

A $-87 + (-68) + (-13)$

SOLUTION
Use the commutative property to change the order of -87 and -68. Then use the associative property to group -87 and -13.

$$-87 + (-68) + (-13) = -68 + (-87) + (-13)$$
$$= -68 + (-87 + (-13))$$
$$= -68 + (-100)$$
$$= -168$$

B $-36 + 419 + 136$

SOLUTION
Use the commutative property to change the order of 419 and 136. Then add from left to right.

$$-36 + 419 + 136 = -36 + 136 + 419$$
$$= 100 + 419$$
$$= 519 \ \blacksquare$$

Rewriting Subtraction as Addition to Use Addition Properties

The commutative and associative properties do not apply to subtraction. These examples illustrate this rule.

$$3 - 1 \overset{?}{=} 1 - 3 \qquad (8 - 2) - 5 \overset{?}{=} 8 - (2 - 5)$$
$$2 \neq -2 \qquad\qquad 6 - 5 \overset{?}{=} 8 - (-3)$$
$$1 \neq 11$$

However, by rewriting a subtraction expression as addition of the opposite, you can use the commutative and associative properties of addition.

EXAMPLE 3

Rewrite the expression using addition only. Then use addition properties so that you can evaluate the expression with mental math.

A $-18 + 34 - 12$

SOLUTION

$$-18 + 34 - \mathbf{12} = -18 + 34 + \mathbf{(-12)} \qquad \text{To subtract 12, add } -12.$$
$$= -18 + (-12) + 34 \qquad \text{Use the commutative property.}$$
$$= -30 + 34 \qquad\qquad \text{Then add from left to right.}$$
$$= 4$$

B $42 - 27 + 8 - 3$

SOLUTION

$$42 - \mathbf{27} + 8 - \mathbf{3} = 42 + \mathbf{(-27)} + 8 + \mathbf{(-3)} \qquad \text{Rewrite subtractions as additions.}$$
$$= 42 + 8 + (-27) + (-3) \qquad \text{Use the commutative property.}$$
$$= (42 + 8) + (-27 + (-3)) \qquad \text{Then use the associative property to group}$$
$$\text{numbers that are easier numbers to add.}$$
$$= 50 + (-30)$$
$$= 20 \ \blacksquare$$

Solving Equations by Recognizing Properties of Addition

EXAMPLE 4

Solve the equation.

A $(7 + 4.14) + 8.2 = 7 + (y + 8.2)$

SOLUTION
By the associative property, $(7 + 4.14) + 8.2 = 7 + (\mathbf{4.14} + 8.2)$,
so $y = 4.14$.

B $2 + (-0.4) + 5.06 = 2 + c + (-0.4)$

SOLUTION
By the commutative property, $2 + (-0.4) + 5.06 = 2 + \mathbf{5.06} + (-0.4)$,
so $c = 5.06$.

C $-(-5 + 4) - 5 + x$

SOLUTION
By the property of the opposite of a sum, you know that
$-(-5 + 4) = \mathbf{5} + (-4)$, so $x = -4$. ■

> ▶ **Remember** The opposite of a negative number is positive.
> In Example 4C, the opposite of -5 is 5.

Application: Inventory

EXAMPLE 5

An inventory is a record of the number or amount of something. A librarian keeps track of the change in her inventory of books, as shown in the table. What is the net change in inventory for the week? Explain your steps.

Day of the week	Change in inventory
Monday	$+30$
Tuesday	-27
Wednesday	$+14$
Thursday	$+26$
Friday	-3

SOLUTION

$$
\begin{aligned}
30 + (-27) + 14 + 26 + (-3) &= 30 + (-27) + (-3) + 14 + 26 \\
&= 30 + (-27 + (-3)) + (14 + 26) \\
&= 30 + (-30) + 40 \\
&= 0 + 40 \\
&= 40
\end{aligned}
$$

The commutative property is used to change the order of the addends so that -27 and -3 are together from left to right. Then the associative property is used to group -27 and -3 as well as 14 and 26. Then the additions inside grouping symbols are performed. Finally the numbers are added from left to right. The net change in inventory is $+40$. ■

Distances Between Rationals

The distance between two points on a number line is equal to the absolute value of the difference of their coordinates.

Distance Between Points on a Number Line

Distance Between Two Points

The distance between two distinct points is a positive number. The formula for finding the distance between two points with coordinates p and q is

$$|p - q|.$$

You can use a number line to show that the distance between two different points is the same no matter which direction you travel.

Modeling a Real-World Distance Problem

You can use a number line to model the distance between two numbers. Plot the points on a number line, and then compute their difference.

EXAMPLE

Brandon's dog is $10\frac{1}{2}$ in. tall. His parakeet is $6\frac{3}{4}$ in. tall.

A Represent the equations on a number line. Show how each equation relates to the pets' heights.

$$10\frac{1}{2} - 6\frac{3}{4} = 3\frac{3}{4}$$

$$6\frac{3}{4} - 10\frac{1}{2} = -3\frac{3}{4}$$

SOLUTION

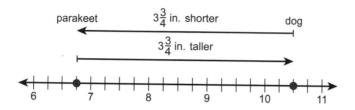

The difference $10\frac{1}{2} - 6\frac{3}{4} = 3\frac{3}{4}$ is positive, so it represents how much taller the dog is than the parakeet. The difference $6\frac{3}{4} - 10\frac{1}{2} = -3\frac{3}{4}$ is negative, so it represents how much shorter the parakeet is than the dog.

B Difference in height is commonly expressed as a number greater than or equal to 0, not as a negative number. How would you write an equation to ensure the pets' difference in height is a positive number, no matter what order the numbers are subtracted in? Explain your reasoning.

SOLUTION

Begin with the equations in Example A. Take the absolute value of each difference to ensure that the expressions each simplify to a positive number.

$$\left|10\frac{1}{2} - 6\frac{3}{4}\right| = 3\frac{3}{4}$$

$$\left|6\frac{3}{4} - 10\frac{1}{2}\right| = \left|-3\frac{3}{4}\right| = 3\frac{3}{4} \ \blacksquare$$

Multiplying and Dividing Rational Numbers

Topic List

More than 200,000 zebras migrate between the Serengeti in Tanzania and the Maasai Mara in Kenya every year. How many will make it across the Mara River, and how long will it take them? Scientists use operations with rational numbers to understand zebra behavior and health.

Multiplying Integers, Decimals, and Fractions

The result of multiplying two or more factors together is the product.

Multiplying Integers

To find the **product** of two or more nonzero numbers, use these steps.

How to Multiply Nonzero Numbers

Step 1 Ignore the signs of the numbers. Multiply as usual.

Step 2 Give the product a sign.

- The product of two positive factors is positive.
- The product of two negative factors is positive.
- The product of a negative factor and a positive factor is negative.

Sign of the Product $a \cdot b$

	a positive	a negative
b positive	$+$	$-$
b negative	$-$	$+$

▶ **Think About It** The rules can also be stated this way:

If the signs are the same, the product is positive.

If the signs are different, the product is negative.

EXAMPLE 1

Multiply.

A 3 • 8

SOLUTION

3 • 8 = 24   Multiply. Both factors are positive. The product is positive.

B −4 • (−7)

SOLUTION

−4 • (−7) = +28   Multiply. Both factors are negative. The product is positive.

C −9 • 5

SOLUTION

9 • 5 = 45   Multiply. One factor is negative. The other is positive.
                The product is negative. ▪

Multiplying Decimals

Use the same rules to multiply decimals.

EXAMPLE 2

Multiply.

A −0.2 • (−6.5)

SOLUTION

$$
\begin{array}{r}
\overset{1}{6.5} \\
\times\ 0.2 \\
\hline
1.30
\end{array}
$$
    Multiply 0.2 × 6.5.

−0.2 • (−6.5) = 1.30   Both factors are negative. The product is positive.

B $4.2 \cdot (-1.3)$

SOLUTION

$$\begin{array}{r} 4.2 \\ \times\,-1.3 \\ \hline 1\,2\,6 \\ 4\,2\,0 \\ \hline -5.4\,6 \end{array}$$

Multiply $4.2 \cdot (-1.3)$.

$4.2 \cdot (-1.3) = -5.46$ One factor is positive. The other factor is negative. The product is negative. ■

Multiplying Fractions

Use the same rules to multiply fractions.

EXAMPLE 3

A $\dfrac{3}{8} \cdot \left(-\dfrac{2}{5}\right)$

SOLUTION

$\dfrac{3}{8} \cdot \left(\dfrac{2}{5}\right) = \dfrac{6}{40}$ Multiply as usual, ignoring the signs..

$\dfrac{6 \div 2}{40 \div 2} = \dfrac{3}{20}$ Simplify.

$\dfrac{3}{8} \cdot \left(-\dfrac{2}{5}\right) = -\dfrac{3}{20}$ One fraction is positive. The other fraction is negative. The product is negative.

B $-\dfrac{1}{3} \cdot \left(-2\dfrac{3}{4}\right)$

SOLUTION

$\dfrac{1}{3} \cdot \left(2\dfrac{3}{4}\right) = \dfrac{1}{3} \cdot \left(\dfrac{11}{4}\right)$ Ignore the signs and rewrite the mixed number.

$= \dfrac{11}{12}$ Multiply.

$-\dfrac{1}{3} \cdot \left(-2\dfrac{3}{4}\right) = \dfrac{11}{12}$ Both fractions are negative. The product is positive. ■

Multiplying Three or More Factors

To find the product of three or more factors, multiply one pair of factors. Then multiply their product by the next factor. Keep going until you have used every factor.

EXAMPLE 4

Multiply.

$$-8 \cdot 2 \cdot (-3)$$

SOLUTION

$$-8 \cdot 2 \cdot (-3) = -16 \cdot (-3) \qquad \text{Multiply the first two factors.}$$
$$= 48 \qquad \text{Multiply the product by the third factor.} \blacksquare$$

> ▶ **Think About It** You can choose any pair of factors to multiply first. The final answer will be the same. For example,
> $$-8 \cdot 2 \cdot (-3) = -8 \cdot (-6)$$
> $$= 48$$

Simplifying and Evaluating Expressions

EXAMPLE 5

Simplify.

$$3 + (-2) \cdot 6$$

SOLUTION

$$3 + (-2) \cdot 6 = 3 + (-12) \qquad \text{Multiply. The product is negative.}$$
$$= -9 \qquad \text{Add.} \blacksquare$$

> ▶ **Think About It** When simplifying an expression, only do one step at a time.

EXAMPLE 6

Evaluate $3x - 4$ when $x = -7$.

SOLUTION

$$3x - 4 = 3 \cdot (-7) - 4 \qquad \text{Substitute } -7 \text{ for } x.$$

$$= -21 - 4 \qquad \text{Multiply.}$$

$$= -25 \qquad \text{Subtract.} \ \blacksquare$$

Determining the Sign of the Product of Several Factors

When you multiply three or more nonzero factors, you can determine the sign of the product by counting the number of negative factors. Every pair of negative factors makes a positive, which means that

- If the number of negative factors is even, the product is positive.

- If the number of negative factors is odd, the product is negative.

EXAMPLE 7

Give the sign of the product. Write *positive* or *negative*.

A $-6 \cdot 0.5 \cdot (-2) \cdot (-4) \cdot (-1)$

SOLUTION

$-6 \cdot 0.5 \cdot (-2) \cdot (-4) \cdot (-1)$ There are four negative factors.
The product is positive.

B $(-3)^5$

SOLUTION

$(-3)^5 = (-3) \cdot (-3) \cdot (-3) \cdot (-3) \cdot (-3)$ There are five negative factors.
The product is negative. ▪

▶ **Remember** An exponent tells how many times the base is used as a factor.

Problem Solving with Multiplication of Rational Numbers

You can solve real-world problems using multiplication, even when factors have different signs. The same rules apply for determining the sign of the product.

EXAMPLE 8

A The water level in a lake changed $-\frac{3}{4}$ ft over 1 wk because of a drought. The water level dropped $\frac{1}{2}$ of that amount the next week. What was the change in water level in the second week of the drought?

> ▶ **Remember** The word *of* in a word problem indicates multiplication.

SOLUTION

$$-\frac{3}{4} \cdot \frac{1}{2} = -\frac{3}{8}$$ There is one positive factor and one negative factor. The product is negative.

The second week of the drought, the water level changed $-\frac{3}{8}$ ft.

B A student is charged a fee of $0.10 per day for a late library book. He accidentally returns the book 2.5 wk late. How much does he owe?

> ▶ **Think About It** A fee represents an amount of money that is paid or lost. Therefore, a fee of $0.10 represents a negative value.

SOLUTION

Multiply the amount the student is charged per day, the number of days in a week, and the weeks the book is overdue to find the total.

$-0.10 \cdot 7 \cdot 2.5 = -0.70 \cdot 2.5$ Multiply the first two factors.

$= -1.75$ Multiply the product by the third factor.

The student owes $1.75 for returning his book 2.5 wk late. ▪

Dividing Integers and Decimals

The result of division is the **quotient**.

Dividing Integers and Decimals

If you can divide positive numbers, you can divide positive and negative numbers. The steps for the sign of a quotient are the same as the steps for the sign of a product.

How to Divide Nonzero Numbers

Step 1 Ignore the signs of the numbers. Divide as usual.

Step 2 Give the quotient a sign.

- The quotient of two positive numbers is positive.
- The quotient of two negative numbers is positive.
- The quotient of a negative number and a positive number is negative.

Sign of the Quotient $a \div b$

	a positive	a negative
b positive	$+$	$-$
b negative	$-$	$+$

> ▶ **Think About It** The rules for signs when multiplying and dividing nonzero numbers are the same.

EXAMPLE 1

Divide.

A $-12 \div 3$

SOLUTION

$-12 \div 3 = -4$ Divide. One number is negative. The other number is positive. The quotient is negative.

B $-5.5 \div (-1.1)$

SOLUTION

$-5.5 \div (-1.1) = 5$ Divide. Both numbers are negative. The quotient is positive.

C $6 : 1.5$

SOLUTION

$6 \div 1.5 = 4$ Divide. Both numbers are positive. The quotient is positive. ▪

Simplifying and Evaluating Expressions

EXAMPLE 2

Simplify.

$$\frac{12}{-4 + 2}$$

SOLUTION

$\dfrac{12}{-4 + 2} = \dfrac{12}{-2}$ Simplify the denominator.

$\phantom{\dfrac{12}{-4 + 2}} = -6$ Divide. ▪

EXAMPLE 3

Evaluate $0.6b \div (0.2 - 0.5)$ when $b = 4$.

SOLUTION

$$0.6b \div (0.2 - 0.5) = (0.6 \cdot 4) \div (0.2 - 0.5) \qquad \text{Substitute 4 for } b.$$

$$= 2.4 \div (-0.3) \qquad \text{Multiply and subtract inside parentheses.}$$

$$= -8 \qquad \text{Divide.} \blacksquare$$

Finding the Mean of Signed Numbers

The mean or average of a set of values is found by adding the numbers, then dividing by the number of values.

EXAMPLE 4

Find the mean of the set of numbers.

$$-3, 5, 0, 2, -1.5, -4$$

SOLUTION

There are six values, so to find the mean, divide the sum of the values by 6.

$$\frac{-3 + 5 + 0 + 2 + (-1.5) + (-4)}{6} = \frac{-1.5}{6} \qquad \text{Simplify the numerator.}$$

$$= -\frac{1}{4} \qquad \text{Divide.} \blacksquare$$

Dividing Fractions

Division separates a number into equal groups.

Sometimes the divisor and dividend are fractions.

This figure illustrates $\frac{2}{3}$ of a whole.

This area is $\frac{1}{6}$ of the whole.

There are four $\frac{1}{6}$ in $\frac{2}{3}$. That is, $\frac{2}{3} \div \frac{1}{6} = 4$,

Finding Reciprocals of Fractions

The reciprocal of $\dfrac{a}{b} = \dfrac{1}{\dfrac{a}{b}}$ The reciprocal of any number is 1 over the number.

$$= \dfrac{1}{\dfrac{a}{b}} \cdot \dfrac{b}{b}$$ Multiply the numerator and denominator by b so there will no longer be a fraction in the bottom.

$$= \dfrac{1 \cdot b}{\dfrac{a \cdot \cancel{b}}{\cancel{b}}}$$

$$= \dfrac{b}{a}$$

▶ **Remember** The reciprocal is also called the multiplicative inverse because when you multiply a number and its reciprocal, the product is 1.

Reciprocal of a Fraction

For any nonzero a and b,

the reciprocal of $\frac{a}{b}$ is $\frac{b}{a}$.

Example

The reciprocal of $\frac{2}{3}$ is $\frac{3}{2}$.

EXAMPLE 1

Find the reciprocal of the number.

A $\frac{9}{10}$

SOLUTION

The reciprocal is $\frac{10}{9}$.

▶ **Think About It** To find a reciprocal, "flip" the fraction. Check your answer by multiplying.

$$\frac{9}{10} \cdot \frac{10}{9} = \frac{90}{90} = 1$$

B $\frac{1}{5}$

SOLUTION

The reciprocal is $\frac{5}{1}$, or 5. ∎

To divide fractions, multiply the dividend by the reciprocal of the divisor.

▶ **Remember** In $x \div y$, x is the dividend and y is the divisor.

Dividing Fractions	
Property	**Example**
$\dfrac{a}{b} \div \dfrac{c}{d} = \dfrac{a}{b} \cdot \dfrac{d}{c} = \dfrac{ad}{bc}$	$\dfrac{2}{3} \div \dfrac{1}{6} = \dfrac{2}{3} \cdot \dfrac{6}{1} = \dfrac{12}{3} = 4$
$b \neq 0, c \neq 0, d \neq 0$	

Dividing Fractions

EXAMPLE 2

Find the quotient and simplify.

A $\dfrac{1}{2} \div \dfrac{4}{6}$

SOLUTION

$\dfrac{1}{2} \div \dfrac{4}{6} = \dfrac{1}{2} \cdot \dfrac{6}{4}$ Multiply by the reciprocal.

$= \dfrac{1 \cdot 6}{2 \cdot 4}$ Multiply the numerators and the denominators.

$= \dfrac{6}{8}$ Multiply.

$= \dfrac{3}{4}$ Write in simplest form.

B $-8 \div \dfrac{1}{4}$

SOLUTION

$-8 \div \dfrac{1}{4} = 8 \cdot \dfrac{4}{1}$ Multiply by the reciprocal.

$= -8 \cdot 4$ Write $\dfrac{4}{1}$ as 4.

$= -32$ Multiply.

C $\dfrac{2}{3} \div 6$

SOLUTION

$$\dfrac{2}{3} \div 6 = \dfrac{2}{3} \cdot \dfrac{1}{6} \qquad \text{Multiply by the reciprocal.}$$

$$= \dfrac{2 \cdot 1}{3 \cdot 6} \qquad \text{Multiply the numerators and the denominators.}$$

$$= \dfrac{2}{18} \qquad \text{Multiply.}$$

$$= \dfrac{1}{9} \qquad \text{Write in simplest form.}$$

D $\dfrac{5}{x} \div \dfrac{10}{y}$

SOLUTION

$$\dfrac{5}{x} \div \dfrac{10}{y} = \dfrac{\overset{1}{\cancel{5}}}{x} \cdot \dfrac{y}{\underset{2}{\cancel{10}}} \qquad \text{Multiply by the reciprocal. Divide out the common factor of 5.}$$

$$= \dfrac{y}{2x} \qquad \text{Multiply.} \blacksquare$$

Application: Sewing

EXAMPLE 3

Three-fourths of a yard of fabric is divided into 6 sections, each with equal length. How long is each section?

SOLUTION
Divide.

$$\frac{3}{4} \div 6 = \frac{\overset{1}{\cancel{3}}}{4} \cdot \frac{1}{\underset{2}{\cancel{6}}}$$ Multiply by the reciprocal. Divide out the common factor of 3.

$$= \frac{1}{8}$$ Multiply.

Each section is $\frac{1}{8}$ yd long.

CHECK
If each section is $\frac{1}{8}$ yd long, then the total length should be

$$6 \cdot \frac{1}{8} = \frac{6}{8} = \frac{3}{4} \text{ yd.} \checkmark$$

The solution checks. ■

Multiplying and Dividing with Mixed Numbers

You will use your skills of multiplying and dividing fractions to multiply and divide mixed numbers.

To multiply mixed numbers, change each mixed number to an improper fraction. Then multiply the numerators, multiply the denominators, and write the product in simplest form.

Multiplying Mixed Numbers

EXAMPLE 1

Multiply. Write the product as either an integer or a mixed number in simplest form.

A $3 \cdot 2\frac{1}{2}$

SOLUTION

$$3 \cdot 2\frac{1}{2} = \frac{3}{1} \cdot \frac{5}{2} \qquad \text{Write each factor as an improper fraction.}$$

$$= \frac{15}{2} \qquad \text{Multiply.}$$

$$= 7\frac{1}{2} \qquad \text{Convert the answer to a mixed number.}$$

▶ **Think About It** Since $3 \geq 1$, $\frac{3}{1}$ is an improper fraction.

B $2\frac{2}{3} \cdot 4\frac{4}{5}$

SOLUTION

Write each factor as an improper fraction.

$2\frac{2}{3} \cdot 4\frac{4}{5} = \frac{8}{\overset{}{\underset{1}{\cancel{3}}}} \cdot \frac{\overset{8}{\cancel{24}}}{5}$ Divide out the common factor of 3.

$\qquad\quad = \frac{64}{5}$ Multiply.

$\qquad\quad = 12\frac{4}{5}$ Convert the answer to a mixed number.

C $6\frac{1}{7} \cdot (-7)$

SOLUTION

Write each factor as an improper fraction.

$6\frac{1}{7} \cdot (-7) = \frac{43}{\overset{}{\underset{1}{\cancel{7}}}} \cdot \left(-\frac{\overset{1}{\cancel{7}}}{1}\right)$ Divide out the common factor of 7.

$\qquad\qquad = -\frac{43}{1}$ Multiply.

$\qquad\qquad = -43$ Simplify. ■

Dividing Mixed Numbers

Dividing mixed numbers is like multiplying. Start by changing the mixed numbers to improper fractions. Next, change division to multiplying by the reciprocal.

EXAMPLE 2

Divide. Write the quotient as either an integer or a mixed number in simplest form.

A $-5\frac{2}{3} \div \left(-2\frac{1}{2}\right)$

SOLUTION

$-5\frac{2}{3} \div \left(-2\frac{1}{2}\right) = -\frac{17}{3} \div \left(-\frac{5}{2}\right)$ Write each factor as an improper fraction.

$= -\frac{17}{3} \cdot \left(-\frac{2}{5}\right)$ Multiply by the reciprocal of $-\frac{5}{2}$.

$= \frac{34}{15}$ Multiply. Both factors are negative, so the product is positive.

$= 2\frac{4}{15}$ Convert the answer to a mixed number.

B $6\frac{1}{2} \div 2$

SOLUTION

$6\frac{1}{2} \div 2 = \frac{13}{2} \div \frac{2}{1}$ Write each factor as an improper fraction.

$= \frac{13}{2} \cdot \frac{1}{2}$ Multiply by the reciprocal of $\frac{2}{1}$.

$= \frac{13}{4}$ Multiply.

$= 3\frac{1}{4}$ Convert the answer to a mixed number.

▶ **Think About It** Estimate to check your answer for reasonableness.

In Example 2B, $6 \div 2 = 3$ and $7 \div 2 = 3\frac{1}{2}$.

C $\frac{a}{b} \div 3\frac{3}{4}$

SOLUTION

$\frac{a}{b} \div 3\frac{3}{4} = \frac{a}{b} \div \frac{15}{4}$ Write the mixed number as an improper fraction.

$= \frac{a}{b} \cdot \frac{4}{15}$ Multiply by the reciprocal of $\frac{15}{4}$.

$= \frac{4a}{15b}$ Apply the commutative property of multiplication. ■

Application: Catering

EXAMPLE 3

A A recipe serves 6 people. Carla needs to serve 18 people. If the recipe calls for $1\frac{3}{4}$ cups of flour, how much flour will Carla need?

SOLUTION

Carla needs to triple every ingredient because 18 people is 3 times the number of people her recipe will serve.

$1\frac{3}{4} \cdot 3 = \frac{7}{4} \cdot \frac{3}{1}$ Write the factors as improper fractions.

$= \frac{21}{4}$ Multiply.

$= 5\frac{1}{4}$ Convert the improper fraction to a mixed number.

She needs $5\frac{1}{4}$ cups of flour.

B A recipe that serves 4 people calls for $1\frac{1}{3}$ cups of flour. Carla has $9\frac{1}{3}$ cups of flour. How many people can Carla serve?

SOLUTION

Divide to find by how much she can multiply the recipe.

$$9\frac{1}{3} \div 1\frac{1}{3} = \frac{28}{3} \div \frac{4}{3} \qquad \text{Write the mixed numbers as improper fractions.}$$

$$= \frac{\overset{7}{\cancel{28}}}{\underset{1}{\cancel{3}}} \cdot \frac{\overset{1}{\cancel{3}}}{\underset{1}{\cancel{4}}} \qquad \text{Multiply by the reciprocal of } \frac{4}{3}.$$

$$= \frac{7}{1} \qquad \text{Multiply.}$$

$$= 7 \qquad \text{Simplify.}$$

Carla can multiply the recipe by 7. Multiply to find the maximum number of people Carla can serve.

$$7 \cdot 4 = 28$$

Carla can serve 28 people. ■

Multiplication Properties

There are three properties you can use to help you solve multiplication problems.

Multiplication Properties

Property	Example
Associative Property of Multiplication $(a \bullet b) \bullet c = a \bullet (b \bullet c)$	$(2 \bullet 3) \bullet 4 = 2 \bullet (3 \bullet 4)$
Commutative Property of Multiplication $a \bullet b = b \bullet a$	$5 \bullet 7 = 7 \bullet 5$
Distributive of Multiplication $a(b + c) = ab + ac$	$2(6 + 7) = 2(6) + 2(7)$

EXAMPLE 1

Simplify.

$$3.2 \bullet (5 \bullet 5.7)$$

SOLUTION
Use the associative property of multiplication.

$3.2 \bullet (5 \bullet 5.7) = (3.2 \bullet 5) \bullet 5.7$ Group numbers that are easier to multiply.

$\qquad\qquad\qquad = 16 \bullet 5.7$ Multiply inside parentheses.

$\qquad\qquad\qquad = 91.2$ Multiply.

$3.2 \bullet (5 \bullet 5.7) = 91.2$ ■

EXAMPLE 2

Simplify.

$$\frac{4}{15} \cdot \frac{1}{3} \cdot \frac{5}{16}$$

SOLUTION

Use the commutative property of multiplication to rearrange the fractions. Simplify before multiplying.

> ▶ **Think About It** Look for common factors between numerators and denominators. Doing this first makes the multiplication easier.

$$\frac{4}{15} \cdot \frac{1}{3} \cdot \frac{5}{16} = \frac{4}{15} \cdot \frac{5}{16} \cdot \frac{1}{3} \qquad \text{Apply commutative property of multiplication.}$$

$$= \frac{\overset{1}{\cancel{4}}}{\underset{3}{\cancel{15}}} \cdot \frac{\overset{1}{\cancel{5}}}{\underset{4}{\cancel{16}}} \cdot \frac{1}{3} \qquad \text{Divide out common factors.}$$

$$= \frac{1}{36} \qquad\qquad \text{Multiply.}$$

$$\frac{4}{15} \cdot \frac{1}{3} \cdot \frac{5}{16} = \frac{1}{36} \ \blacksquare$$

Notice that although the commutative property works for multiplication, it does not apply to division.

$$\frac{1}{3} \div \frac{1}{2} \neq \frac{1}{2} \div \frac{1}{3}$$

Instead, for a division problem, rewrite the problem as a multiplication problem by using the multiplicative inverse. Then use the multiplication properties as needed.

$$\frac{1}{3} \div \frac{1}{2} = \frac{1}{3} \cdot \frac{2}{1} \qquad \text{Rewrite using the multiplicative inverse.}$$

$$\frac{1}{3} \cdot \frac{2}{1} = \frac{2}{1} \cdot \frac{1}{3} \qquad \text{Apply commutative property of multiplication.} \ \blacksquare$$

EXAMPLE 3

Simplify.

$$\frac{1}{2}\left(\frac{3}{4}+\frac{2}{3}\right)$$

SOLUTION

Use the distributive property of multiplication.

$$\frac{1}{2}\left(\frac{3}{4}+\frac{2}{3}\right) = \frac{1}{2}\left(\frac{3}{4}\right) + \frac{1}{2}\left(\frac{2}{3}\right) \qquad \text{Distribute the factor.}$$

$$= \frac{3}{8} + \frac{2}{6} \qquad \text{Multiply.}$$

$$= \frac{9}{24} + \frac{8}{24} \qquad \text{Rewrite using a common denominator.}$$

$$= \frac{17}{24} \qquad \text{Add.}$$

$$\frac{1}{2}\left(\frac{3}{4}+\frac{2}{3}\right) = \frac{17}{24} \quad \blacksquare$$

EXAMPLE 4

Evaluate.

$$(-4) \cdot \frac{2}{3} \cdot 2 \div \frac{1}{3}$$

SOLUTION

Rewrite the problem using only multiplication. Then use the properties of multiplication to evaluate.

▶ **Remember** The multiplicative inverse of $\frac{a}{b}$ is $\frac{b}{a}$.

$(-4) \cdot \dfrac{2}{3} \cdot 2 \div \dfrac{1}{3} = (-4) \cdot \dfrac{2}{3} \cdot 2 \cdot \dfrac{3}{1}$ Rewrite using the multiplicative inverse.

$= (-4) \cdot \dfrac{2}{3} \cdot \dfrac{3}{1} \cdot 2$ Commutative Property of Multiplication

$= (-4) \cdot \dfrac{2}{\overset{}{\cancel{3}}_{1}} \cdot \dfrac{\overset{1}{\cancel{3}}}{1} \cdot 2$ Divide out the common factor of 3.

$= (-4) \cdot \dfrac{2}{1} \cdot 2$ Multiply.

$= (-4) \cdot (2 \cdot 2)$ Associative Property of Multiplication

$= (-4) \cdot 4$ Multiply inside parentheses.

$= -16$ Multiply. The product is negative.

$$(-4) \cdot \dfrac{2}{3} \cdot 2 \div \dfrac{1}{3} = -16 \ \blacksquare$$

Decimal Forms of Rational Numbers

Any rational number can be written as a decimal. The digits after the decimal point will either terminate or repeat.

Repeating Decimals

Definition
A decimal is a **repeating decimal** if a digit or a group of digits, other than 0, repeats forever after the decimal point.

Convert a rational number to a decimal by first rewriting the rational number as the ratio of two integers. Use long division to divide the numerator by the denominator. Examine the quotient to see if a digit or group of digits repeats.

EXAMPLE 1

Use long division to show that $\frac{14}{33}$ is a repeating decimal.

SOLUTION

$$
\begin{array}{r}
0.4242 \\
33\overline{)14.0000} \\
\underline{13\,2} \\
80 \\
\underline{66} \\
140 \\
\underline{132} \\
80 \\
\underline{66} \\
140
\end{array}
$$

$\frac{14}{33} = 0.\overline{42}$; The digit pair 42 will repeat forever after the decimal point because the remainder after dividing by 33 will alternate between 14 and 8 without end. ■

Terminating Decimals

Definition
A decimal is a **terminating decimal** if it has a finite number of digits.

Convert a fraction to a decimal by using long division to divide the numerator by the denominator. If the quotient eventually goes evenly into the remainder, the decimal terminates.

EXAMPLE 2

A Convert $\frac{29}{40}$ to a decimal.

SOLUTION

Divide 29 by 40 using long division.

$$
\begin{array}{r}
0.725 \\
40\overline{)29.000} \\
\underline{28\ 0} \\
1\ 00 \\
\underline{80} \\
200 \\
\underline{200} \\
0
\end{array}
$$

The fraction $\frac{29}{40}$ is equivalent to the decimal 0.725.

B Rewrite the quotient you found in Example 2A as a ratio of two integers using a power of 10 for the denominator. Also, explain how this ratio is a fraction equivalent to $\dfrac{29}{40}$.

SOLUTION

First write the quotient as a fraction with the numerator equal to the quotient and the denominator equal to 1. Then convert the numerator to an integer by moving the decimal point three places to the right. To do this, multiply the fraction by 1000 over 1000.

$$\frac{0.725}{1} = \frac{0.725}{1} \cdot \frac{1000}{1000} = \frac{0.725 \cdot 1000}{1 \cdot 1000} = \frac{725}{1000}$$

The fraction $\dfrac{725}{1000}$ can be simplified by dividing both the numerator and denominator by a common factor of 25.

$$\frac{725}{1000} = \frac{725 \div 25}{1000 \div 25} = \frac{29}{40}$$

Since $\dfrac{29}{40}$ is a simplified form of $\dfrac{725}{1000}$, both fractions are equivalent. ▪

Problem Solving with Rational Numbers

You can use rational numbers in the form of both fractions and decimals to solve real-world problems. Convert word problems to equations using the correct signs and operations, and then simplify to solve.

Problem Solving with Fractions

EXAMPLE 1

A Kara used $\frac{5}{8}$ cup of flour to make a batch of muffins and $\frac{1}{2}$ cup of flour to make a batch of bread. How much flour did Kara use in all?

SOLUTION

First find a common denominator. Then add to find the total amount of flour Kara used.

$$\frac{5}{8} + \frac{1}{2} = \frac{5}{8} + \frac{4}{8} \qquad \text{Find a common denominator.}$$

$$= \frac{9}{8} \qquad \text{Add.}$$

$$= 1\frac{1}{8} \qquad \text{Convert the answer to a mixed number.}$$

Kara used $1\frac{1}{8}$ cups of flour.

B Kyle ran $1\frac{1}{2}$ mi the first day of track practice and $2\frac{2}{3}$ mi the second day. How much farther did Kyle run on the second day of practice than on the first day?

SOLUTION

Change each mixed number to an improper fraction. Find a common denominator, and rewrite the improper fractions. Then subtract to find the difference.

> ▶ **Remember** To change a mixed number to an improper fraction, first multiply the denominator by the whole number. Then add the numerator. Write the sum as the numerator of the improper fraction, keeping the denominator the same.

$$2\frac{2}{3} - 1\frac{1}{2} = \frac{8}{3} - \frac{3}{2} \qquad \text{Change the mixed numbers to improper fractions.}$$

$$= \frac{16}{6} - \frac{9}{6} \qquad \text{Rewite the fractions using a common denominator.}$$

$$= \frac{7}{6} \qquad \text{Subtract.}$$

$$- 1\frac{1}{6} \qquad \text{Convert the answer to a mixed number}$$

Kyle ran $1\frac{1}{6}$ mi farther on the second day of practice. ■

EXAMPLE 2

A Maya has $\frac{3}{4}$ lb of fudge. She wants to split it evenly between herself and two friends. How can Maya divide the fudge so that each person gets $\frac{1}{3}$ of the total amount?

> ▶ **Remember** The word *of* in a word problem indicates multiplication.

SOLUTION

Multiply the amounts given in the problem to solve.

$$\frac{3}{4} \cdot \frac{1}{3} = \frac{3}{12} \qquad \text{Multiply.}$$

$$= \frac{1}{4} \qquad \text{Simplify.}$$

Each person gets $\frac{1}{4}$ lb of fudge.

B A box of granola has $\frac{3}{8}$ cup remaining. How many $\frac{1}{4}$ cup servings does the box contain?

SOLUTION

Divide to find how many $\frac{1}{4}$ cup servings are in $\frac{3}{8}$ cup.

$$\frac{3}{8} \div \frac{1}{4} = \frac{3}{8} \cdot \frac{4}{1} \qquad \text{Multiply by the reciprocal of } \frac{1}{4}.$$

$$= \frac{12}{8} \qquad \text{Multiply.}$$

$$= \frac{3}{2} \qquad \text{Simplify.}$$

$$= 1\frac{1}{2} \qquad \text{Convert the answer to a mixed number.}$$

There are $1\frac{1}{2}$ servings left in the box of granola. ∎

Problem Solving with Decimals

EXAMPLE 3

A One week the price of gas increased by 41.25¢/gal. The following week it decreased by 52.15¢/gal. What was the total change in the price of gas over the 2 wk period?

> ▶ **Remember** An increase represents a positive value, and a decrease represents a negative value.

SOLUTION

Step 1 Determine the sign of each value given in the problem.

an increase of 41.25: $+41.25$

a decrease of 52.15: -52.15

Step 2 Add. Since the signs are different, find the difference of the absolute values.

▶ **Think About It** The addends have different signs. Because $|41.25|$ is less than $|-52.15|$, the sum will be negative.

$$(-52.15) + 41.25 = -\left(|-52.15| - |41.25|\right) \qquad \text{The sum is negative.}$$
$$= -(52.15 - 41.25) \qquad \text{Evaluate the absolute values.}$$
$$= -10.9 \qquad \text{Subtract.}$$

The total change in the price of gas over 2 wk was -10.9 ¢/gal.

B Nick has two possible routes for walking to school. Route A is 1.25 mi long. Route B is 0.32 mi to the main road and then 0.85 mi to school. He wants to take the shorter route. Which route should he choose?

SOLUTION
Add the two parts of Route B to find the total length of that route.

$$\begin{array}{r} 0.32 \\ +\ 0.85 \\ \hline 1.17 \end{array}$$

Route A is 1.25 mi long. Route B is 1.17 mi long. Nick should take Route B to school because 1.17 mi is a shorter distance than 1.25 mi. ∎

EXAMPLE 4

A The stock market lost an average of 16.5 points per month for 4.5 consecutive months before it started to recover. What was the total change in points over this time period?

> ▶ **Remember** The product of a negative factor and a positive factor is negative.

SOLUTION

Multiply the monthly loss by the number of months to find the total.

$$\begin{array}{r} -16.5 \\ \times 4.5 \\ \hline -74.24 \end{array}$$ 16.5 is negative because it represents a loss.

The total change was −74.25 points. The stock market lost 74.25 points over the 4.5 month period.

B A group of hikers gained 175.85 m of altitude during a 1.4 h hike. What was their average change in elevation per hour to the nearest hundredth?

SOLUTION

Divide the change in altitude by the number of hours to find the average change in elevation per hour. Round to the nearest hundredth.

$$\frac{175.85}{1.4} = 125.61$$

The hikers gained approximately 125.61 m/h. ▪

Applications with Rational Numbers

Calculating the share or portion of a total amount often involves arithmetic using fractions. In these fractions, the numerator or the denominator may be a decimal, not a whole number.

Working with Fractions

EXAMPLE 1

Rod earned $124.80 last week. He saw there were 4 amounts deducted from his paycheck.

Deduction	Amount
local tax	$1.62
state tax	$5.49
SSI (Social Security)	$7.73
Medicare	$1.81

A **Take-home pay** is defined as the amount of a paycheck remaining after deductions. What fraction of Rod's paycheck was take-home pay? Write your answer as a fraction, and then convert this number to the nearest tenth of a percent.

SOLUTION
Total deductions are $1.62 + 5.49 + 7.73 + 1.81 = 16.65$.

Take-home pay is the amount earned minus deductions, so Rod's take-home pay was $124.80 - 16.65 = 108.15$.

The fraction of the amount Rod earned that is take-home pay is

$\frac{108.15}{124.80} \approx 0.867$, which is equivalent to $0.867 \cdot 100\% = 86.7\%$.

B Use the percentage calculated in Example 1A to find Rod's take-home pay this week if he earned $136.74 before deductions.

SOLUTION

Rod's take-home pay is 86.7% of the amount that he earned, so multiply the amount he earned by 0.867.

$$0.867 \cdot 136.74 \approx 118.55$$

Rod's take-home pay this week was $118.55. ■

EXAMPLE 2

Jon has 4 shares in a community farm. There are 81 shares altogether. Each week, Jon gets a portion of the produce harvested based upon his fraction of the total number of shares of the community farm. Last week, the farm harvested the quantities of produce shown in the table.

Produce item	Total harvest (kg)
lettuce	77.1
beets	46.9
cabbage	95.2

A How much of each item should Jon get? Organize your results in a table.

SOLUTION

Jon has 4 out of 81 shares, so he should get $\frac{4}{81}$ of each item of produce.

$$\text{lettuce: } \frac{4}{81} \cdot 77.1 = \frac{308.4}{81} \approx 3.8$$

$$\text{beets: } \frac{4}{81} \cdot 46.9 = \frac{187.6}{81} \approx 2.3$$

$$\text{cabbage: } \frac{4}{81} \cdot 95.2 = \frac{380.8}{81} \approx 4.7$$

Produce item	Jon's share (kg)
lettuce	3.8
beets	2.3
cabbage	4.7

▶ **Think About It** Estimate the product of a fraction and number by finding another fraction that is close in value to the original fraction and simplifies easily. For example,

$$\frac{20}{38} \approx \frac{20}{40} = \frac{1}{2}.$$

B Jon's friend Naomi has double the number of shares that Jon has. How could Naomi estimate the amount of each item she will get? Will this method overestimate or underestimate what Naomi gets?

SOLUTION

Naomi has 8 shares, so she gets $\frac{8}{81}$ of each item. The fraction $\frac{8}{81}$

is close to $\frac{8}{80}$, which is equal to $\frac{1}{10}$. Multiplying by $\frac{1}{10}$ is equivalent to

dividing by 10, so Naomi could divide each item amount by 10 to estimate

how much of each item she will get. Since $\frac{8}{80} > \frac{8}{81}$, this method

overestimates the amount of each item Naomi gets. ■

▶ **Think About It** If two fractions have the same numerator, then the fraction with the larger denominator is the fraction with the lesser value.

Ratios and Rates

Engines mix air and fuel so they can have the perfect combustible mixture. Each mixture can be described with a ratio that represents the mix of fuel and air it contains. Using the correct ratio to get the mix right is important for an engine's performance and efficiency.

Ratios

A ratio shows how one quantity compares in value to another, related quantity.

Writing Ratios

Definition
A **ratio** is a comparison of two quantities by division.

A ratio can be written as a fraction, with a colon, or with the word *to*.

$$\frac{2}{3} \qquad 2 : 3 \qquad 2 \text{ to } 3$$

▶ **Think About It** All these ratios are read as "2 to 3."

Simplifying Ratios

To write a ratio in simplest form, write it as a fraction in simplest form.

EXAMPLE 1

Simplify the ratio. Write your answer in all three forms.

A $\frac{8}{10}$

SOLUTION

Simplify the fraction.

$\frac{8 \div 2}{10 \div 2} = \frac{4}{5}$ Divide the numerator and the denominator by the greatest common factor.

$$\frac{4}{5} \text{ or } 4 : 5 \text{ or } 4 \text{ to } 5$$

B 28 to 4

SOLUTION

Write the ratio as a fraction, and then simplify it.

$$\frac{28}{4} = \frac{28 \div 4}{4 \div 4} = \frac{7}{1}$$

$$\frac{7}{1} \text{ or } 7 : 1 \text{ or } 7 \text{ to } 1$$

C 63 to 27

SOLUTION

Write the ratio as a fraction, and then simplify it.

$\frac{63}{27} = \frac{63 \div 9}{27 \div 9} = \frac{7}{3}$ Don't write a ratio as a mixed number. Write the improper fraction $\frac{7}{3}$.

$$\frac{7}{3} \text{ or } 7 : 3 \text{ or } 7 \text{ to } 3 \ \blacksquare$$

Comparing Parts and Wholes

You can use a ratio to compare a part to a part, a part to a whole, or a whole to a part.

EXAMPLE 2

A jar contains 21 marbles: 8 white, 3 green, and 10 red. Write the described ratio in simplest form.

A number of white marbles to number of green marbles

SOLUTION
There are 8 white marbles and 3 green marbles.

The ratio is $\frac{8}{3}$ or 8 : 3 or 8 to 3.

B number of green marbles to total number of marbles

SOLUTION
There are 3 green marbles and 21 marbles in all.

Since $\frac{3}{21} = \frac{1}{7}$, the ratio is $\frac{1}{7}$ or 1 : 7 or 1 to 7.

C total number of marbles to number of white marbles

SOLUTION
There are 21 marbles in all and 8 white marbles.

The ratio is $\frac{21}{8}$ or 21 : 8 or 21 to 8. ▪

▸ **Think About It** Example 2A compares a part to a part. Example 2B compares a part to a whole. Example 2C compares a whole to a part.

EXAMPLE 3

The table shows the number of sandwiches sold at a lunch truck on 1 day.
Write each ratio in simplest form.

Sandwich	Number sold
veggie sub	13
hamburger	8
hot dog	15

A number of veggie subs sold to hamburgers sold

SOLUTION

There were 13 veggie subs and 8 hamburgers sold.

The ratio is $\frac{13}{8}$ or 13 : 8 or 13 to 8.

B number of hot dogs sold to total number of sandwiches sold

SOLUTION

There were 15 hot dogs sold. The total number of sandwiches sold was
$13 + 8 + 15 = 36$.

The ratio is $\frac{15}{36} = \frac{5}{12}$ or 5 : 12 or 5 to 12.

▶ **Remember** Sometimes you will need to find the sum of all items
to find a part-to-a-whole ratio or a whole-to-a-part ratio.

C total number of sandwiches sold to hamburgers sold

SOLUTION

There were 8 hamburgers sold. The total number of sandwiches sold was
$13 + 8 + 15 = 36$.

The ratio is $\frac{36}{8} = \frac{9}{2}$ or 9 : 2 or 9 to 2. ■

Application: Win-Loss Ratio

EXAMPLE 4

A softball team wins 12 of its 22 games and loses the rest. What is the ratio of wins to losses in simplest form?

SOLUTION

Since $22 - 12 = 10$, the team loses 10 games.

$$\frac{\text{number of wins}}{\text{number of losses}} = \frac{12}{10}$$

$$= \frac{12 \div 2}{10 \div 2} = \frac{6}{5} \qquad \text{Divide by the greatest common factor to simplify the fraction.}$$

The ratio of wins to losses is $\frac{6}{5}$ or 6 : 5 or 6 to 5. ■

> ▶ **Remember** A ratio is not usually written as a mixed number or a decimal, but a ratio can contain a mixed number or a decimal.

Rates

A rate indicates how two related quantities, measured in different units, compare in value.

Writing Rates

Definition
A **rate** is a ratio of quantities that have different units.

To write a rate, write a fraction with the first quantity as the numerator and the second quantity as the denominator. Keep the units with each quantity as you write it

EXAMPLE 1

Write a rate to represent the situation.

A It costs $3 for a 5 min phone call.

SOLUTION

$$\frac{\$3}{5 \text{ min}}$$

B A car travels 85 mi on 4 gal of gasoline.

SOLUTION

$$\frac{85 \text{ mi}}{4 \text{ gal}}$$

Think About It It is also correct, in some contexts, to use the reciprocal as the ratio as well. You could write the ratio $\dfrac{4 \text{ gal}}{85 \text{ mi}}$ for Example 1B.

C Three T-shirts cost $17.50.

SOLUTION

$$\frac{\$17.50}{3 \text{ shirts}}$$

D Two cups of flour are needed to make 14 pancakes.

SOLUTION

$$\frac{2 \text{ cups}}{14 \text{ pancakes}}$$

Finding Unit Rates

Definition
A **unit rate** is a rate in which the second quantity is 1.

How to Find a Unit Rate
Step 1 Separate the units from the number part of the fraction.   **Step 2** Simplify the number part of the fraction.

EXAMPLE 2

Write a unit rate for the situation.

A Mr. Beck drives 120 mi in 3 h.

SOLUTION

Write a ratio. Divide the numerator and the denominator by 3.

$$\frac{120}{3} \cdot \frac{\text{miles}}{\text{hours}} = \frac{120 \div 3}{3 \div 3} \cdot \frac{\text{miles}}{\text{hours}} = \frac{40}{1} \cdot \frac{\text{miles}}{\text{hour}}, \text{ or 40 mph}$$

▶ **Think About It** The abbreviation mph means miles per hour.

B There are 36 servings in 4 bags.

SOLUTION

Write a ratio. Divide the numerator and the denominator by 4.

$$\frac{36}{4} \cdot \frac{\text{servings}}{\text{bags}} = \frac{36 \div 4}{4 \div 4} \cdot \frac{\text{servings}}{\text{bags}} = \frac{9}{1} \cdot \frac{\text{servings}}{\text{bag}}, \text{ or 9 servings/bag}$$

C Ella types 474 words in 6 min.

SOLUTION

Write a ratio. Divide the numerator and the denominator by 6.

$$\frac{474}{6} \cdot \frac{\text{words}}{\text{minutes}} = \frac{474 \div 6}{6 \div 6} \cdot \frac{\text{words}}{\text{minutes}} = \frac{79}{1} \cdot \frac{\text{words}}{\text{minute}}, \text{ or 79 words/min}$$

D Sana earns $104 in 8 h.

SOLUTION

Write a ratio. Divide the numerator and the denominator by 8.

$$\frac{104}{8} \cdot \frac{\text{dollars}}{\text{hours}} = \frac{104 \div 8}{8 \div 8} \cdot \frac{\text{dollars}}{\text{hours}} = \frac{13}{1} \cdot \frac{\text{dollars}}{\text{hour}}, \text{ or \$13/h} \ ■$$

Application: Fuel Economy

EXAMPLE 3

A car travels 255 mi and uses 8.5 gal of gasoline. Write the unit rate that describes the car's fuel economy.

SOLUTION

Write a rate, and then convert it to a unit rate.

$$\frac{255}{8.5} \cdot \frac{\text{miles}}{\text{gallons}} = \frac{255 \div 8.5}{8.5 \div 8.5} \cdot \frac{\text{miles}}{\text{gallons}} = \frac{30}{1} \cdot \frac{\text{miles}}{\text{gallon}}, \text{ or } 30 \text{ mpg}$$

The car's fuel economy is described by the unit rate 30 mpg. ■

▶ **Think About It** The abbreviation mpg means miles per gallon.

Application: Ticket Sales

EXAMPLE 4

The table shows the number of tickets sold at a movie theater and the total sales for each ticket type. Find the unit rate that describes each ticket price.

Ticket type	Number sold	Total sales ($)
adult	12	108.00
senior	15	90.00
youth	7	24.50

SOLUTION

Write a rate for each ticket price, and then simplify the rate to find the unit rate representing the ticket price.

adult: $\frac{108}{12} \cdot \frac{\text{dollars}}{\text{tickets}} = \frac{108 \div 12}{12 \div 12} \cdot \frac{\text{dollars}}{\text{tickets}} = \frac{9}{1} \cdot \frac{\text{dollars}}{\text{ticket}}, \text{ or } \$9/\text{ticket}$

senior: $\frac{90}{15} \cdot \frac{\text{dollars}}{\text{tickets}} = \frac{90 \div 15}{15 \div 15} \cdot \frac{\text{dollars}}{\text{tickets}} = \frac{6}{1} \cdot \frac{\text{dollars}}{\text{ticket}}, \text{ or } \$6/\text{ticket}$

youth: $\frac{24.5}{7} \cdot \frac{\text{dollars}}{\text{tickets}} = \frac{24.5 \div 7}{7 \div 7} \cdot \frac{\text{dollars}}{\text{tickets}} = \frac{3.5}{1} \cdot \frac{\text{dollars}}{\text{ticket}}, \text{ or } \$3.50/\text{ticket}$ ■

▶ **Think About It** Rates with money are often written like $9/ticket, which is the same as 9 dollars per ticket.

Unit Rates

Calculating a unit rate sometimes involves finding the ratio of noninteger values.

Solving Unit Rates Involving Complex Fractions

Definition

A **complex fraction** is a fraction that has fractions in the numerator and/or the denominator.

When either of the quantities in a rate is a fraction or a mixed number, write the rate of the two quantities as a complex fraction. Then simplify the complex fraction to find the unit rate.

EXAMPLE 1

Suppose $2\frac{1}{2}$ lb of apples cost \$6. Write a unit rate representing the amount of apples per dollar.

▶ **Think About It** To simplify a complex fraction, rewrite the fraction as a division problem, and then find the quotient.

SOLUTION

First convert the mixed number to an improper fraction. Then write the rate comparing the two quantities as a fraction and simplify.

$$\frac{2\frac{1}{2}\text{ lb}}{\$6} = \frac{\frac{5}{2}}{6} \cdot \frac{\text{pounds}}{\text{dollars}}$$

$$= \left(\frac{5}{2} \div 6\right) \cdot \frac{\text{pounds}}{\text{dollars}}$$

$$= \left(\frac{5}{2} \cdot \frac{1}{6}\right) \cdot \frac{\text{pounds}}{\text{dollars}}$$

$$= \frac{5}{12} \cdot \frac{\text{pounds}}{\text{dollars}}$$

The unit rate is $\frac{5}{12}$ lb/dollar. ■

EXAMPLE 2

A gazelle took 14 s to run $\frac{1}{4}$ mi. Write a unit rate representing the time it would take the gazelle to run 1 mi.

SOLUTION

Write a rate comparing the time the gazelle ran to the distance covered as a fraction and simplify.

> ▶ **Remember** Either of the two quantities in a rate may have a fractional amount.

$$\frac{14\text{ s}}{\frac{1}{4}\text{ mi}} = \left(14 \div \frac{1}{4}\right) \cdot \frac{\text{seconds}}{\text{miles}}$$

$$= \left(14 \cdot \frac{4}{1}\right) \cdot \frac{\text{seconds}}{\text{miles}}$$

$$= 56 \cdot \frac{\text{seconds}}{\text{mile}}$$

The unit rate is 56 s/mi. ■

EXAMPLE 3

David used $\frac{2}{3}$ gal of paint to cover $\frac{1}{12}$ of a large floor.

Write a unit rate showing the amount of paint David would use to cover 1 full floor.

SOLUTION

$$\frac{\frac{2}{3} \text{ gal}}{\frac{1}{12} \text{ floor}} = \left(\frac{2}{3} \div \frac{1}{12} \right) \cdot \frac{\text{gallons}}{\text{floor}}$$

$$= \left(\frac{2}{3} \cdot \frac{12}{1} \right) \cdot \frac{\text{gallons}}{\text{floor}}$$

$$= \frac{24}{3} \cdot \frac{\text{gallons}}{\text{floor}}$$

$$= 8 \cdot \frac{\text{gallons}}{\text{floor}}$$

The unit rate is 8 gal/floor. ■

Percents, Fractions, and Decimals

Every fraction can be written as an equivalent decimal and as a percent.

A **percent** is a ratio that compares a number to 100. Every percent can be written as a fraction and as a decimal. The table shows a few examples.

Fraction	Decimal	Percent
$\frac{1}{10}$	0.1	10%
$\frac{1}{4}$	0.25	25%
$\frac{1}{2}$	0.5	50%

Converting Fractions to Decimals

A fraction bar can be thought of as a division symbol.

How to Convert a Fraction to a Decimal

For any b and nonzero a,
$\frac{b}{a}$ is equivalent to $b \div a$.

Example

$$\frac{1}{5} = 1 \div 5 = 0.2$$

$$
\begin{array}{r}
0.2 \\
5\overline{)1.0} \\
\underline{10} \\
0
\end{array}
$$

EXAMPLE 1

Convert the fraction to a decimal.

A $\dfrac{3}{8}$

SOLUTION

$$\dfrac{3}{8} = 3 \div 8 = 0.375$$

$$
\begin{array}{r}
0.375 \\
8{\overline{)3.000}} \\
\underline{2\,4} \\
60 \\
\underline{56} \\
40 \\
\underline{40} \\
0
\end{array}
$$

B $\dfrac{2}{3}$

SOLUTION

$$\dfrac{2}{3} = 2 \div 3 = 0.\overline{6}$$

Place a bar over a digit or group of digits to indicate a repeating pattern.

$$
\begin{array}{r}
0.666\ldots \\
3{\overline{)2.000}} \\
\underline{1\,8} \\
20 \\
\underline{18} \\
20 \\
\underline{18} \\
\vdots\ \blacksquare
\end{array}
$$

▶ **Think About It** You could go on forever with this division problem and always end up with another 6.

Converting Decimals to Fractions

Every decimal represents a fraction or a mixed number whose denominator is 10, 100, 1000, or some other power of 10.

How to Convert a Decimal to a Simplified Fraction

Write the decimal as a fraction or a mixed number, and then simplify.

Example

$$0.36 = \frac{36}{100} = \frac{36 \div 4}{100 \div 4} = \frac{9}{25}$$

EXAMPLE 2

Convert the decimal to a fraction or a mixed number. Simplify.

A 0.8

SOLUTION

$$0.8 = \frac{8}{10} = \frac{8 \div 2}{10 \div 2} = \frac{4}{5}$$

B 7.405

SOLUTION

$$7.405 = 7\frac{405}{1000} = 7\frac{405 \div 5}{1000 \div 5} = 7\frac{81}{200} \ \blacksquare$$

Converting Decimals to Percents

To write a decimal as a percent, write a fraction with a denominator of 100. The numerator is the percent. For example, $0.35 = \frac{35}{100} = 35\%$. Notice that you can obtain the answer by just moving the decimal point two places to the right.

> **Think About It** You can write any decimal as a fraction with a denominator of 100 and then a percent.
>
> $$0.625 = \frac{625}{1000}$$
> $$= \frac{625 \div 10}{1000 \div 10}$$
> $$= \frac{62.5}{100}$$
> $$= 62.5\%$$

How to Convert a Decimal to a Percent

Move the decimal point two places to the right and write a percent sign (%).	**Example** $0.35 = 035.\%$ $= 35\%$

EXAMPLE 3

Convert the decimal to a percent.

A 0.72

SOLUTION

$$0.72 = 072.\%$$
$$= 72\%$$

B 5.43

SOLUTION

$$5.43 = 543.\%$$
$$= 543\%$$

C 0.0005

SOLUTION

$$0.0005 = 000.05\,\%$$
$$= 0.05\% \;\blacksquare$$

Converting Percents to Decimals

Because a percent is a ratio with 100 in the denominator, converting a percent to a decimal is the same as dividing by 100.

How to Convert a Percent to a Decimal	
Move the decimal point two places to the left and remove the percent sign (%).	**Example** $68\% = 0.68$ $= 0.68$

EXAMPLE 4

Convert the percent to a decimal.

A 4%

SOLUTION

$$4\% = 0.04$$
$$= 0.04$$

B 127%

SOLUTION

$$127\% = 1.\underset{\smile\smile}{27}$$
$$= 1.27$$

C 0.6%

SOLUTION

$$0.6\% = 0.\underset{\smile\smile}{006}$$
$$= 0.006 \ \blacksquare$$

Converting Fractions to Percents

How to Convert a Fraction to a Percent

Convert the fraction to a decimal, and then convert the decimal to a percent.	**Example** $\dfrac{4}{5} = 4 \div 5 = 0.8 = 80\%$

EXAMPLE 5

Convert the fraction or mixed number to a percent. Round your answer to the nearest percent if rounding is necessary.

A $\dfrac{3}{40}$

SOLUTION

$$\frac{3}{40} = 3 \div 40 = 0.075 = 7.5\%$$

B $2\frac{4}{13}$

SOLUTION

$$2\frac{4}{13} = \frac{30}{13} = 30 \div 13 \approx 2.308 = 230.8\% \approx 231\% \ \blacksquare$$

Converting Percents to Fractions

How to Convert a Percent to a Simplified Fraction

Write the percent as a fraction with a denominator of 100, and then simplify.

Example

$$45\% = \frac{45}{100} = \frac{45 \div 5}{100 \div 5} = \frac{9}{20}$$

EXAMPLE 6

Convert the percent to a fraction or mixed number. Simplify.

A 320%

SOLUTION

$$320\% = \frac{320}{100} = \frac{320 \div 20}{100 \div 20} = \frac{16}{5} = 3\frac{1}{5}$$

> ▶ **Think About It** In Example 6B, you must multiply to eliminate the decimal in the numerator.

B 8.7%

SOLUTION

$$8.7\% = \frac{8.7}{100} = \frac{8.7 \times 10}{100 \times 10} = \frac{87}{1000}$$ ∎

Application: Marketing

EXAMPLE 7

A marketing survey indicates that 18 of 64 people plan to purchase a video game in the next year. To the nearest tenth of a percent, what percent of those surveyed plan to purchase the video game?

SOLUTION

$$\frac{18}{64} = 18 \div 64 = 0.28125 = 28.125\% \approx 28.1\%$$

About 28.1% of those surveyed plan to purchase the video game. ∎

Percent of Increase or Decrease

Percent change is the the extent to which a quantity increases or decreases, expressed as a percent.

Determining Percent of Change

amount of change = new amount − original amount

$$\text{percent of change} = \frac{\text{amount of change}}{\text{original amount}} \cdot 100\%$$

Finding Percent Increase and Decrease

EXAMPLE 1

A Find the percent increase from 10 to 15.

SOLUTION

amount of change = new amount − original amount   Find the amount of change.

$= 15 - 10$ Substitute.

$= 5$

$$\text{percent of change} = \frac{\text{amount of change}}{\text{original amount}} \cdot 100\% \qquad \text{Find the percent of change.}$$

$$= \frac{5}{10} \cdot 100\% \qquad\qquad\qquad \text{Substitute.}$$

$$- 0.5 \cdot 100\% \qquad\qquad\qquad \text{Multiply.}$$

$$= 50\%$$

The percent increase is 50%.

B Find the percent decrease from 15 to 10.

SOLUTION

$$\text{amount of change} = \text{new amount} - \text{original amount} \qquad \text{Find the amount of change.}$$

$$= 10 - 15 \qquad\qquad\qquad \text{Substitute.}$$

$$= -5 \qquad\qquad\qquad \text{Subtract.}$$

$$\text{percent of change} = \frac{\text{amount of change}}{\text{original amount}} \cdot 100\% \qquad \text{Find the percent of change.}$$

$$= -\frac{5}{15} \cdot 100\% \qquad\qquad \text{Substitute.}$$

$$= -\frac{500}{15}\% \qquad\qquad\qquad \text{Simplify.}$$

$$= -33\frac{1}{3}\%$$

The percent decrease is $33\frac{1}{3}\%$. ▪

▶ **Think About It** A percent increase is not offset by the same percent decrease. For example, if an item that costs $10 is marked up to $15, the percent increase is 50%. If that item that costs $15 is discounted to $10, the percent decrease is $33\frac{1}{3}\%$.

EXAMPLE 2

A The population of Smalltown changed from 125 to 150. What was the percent increase?

SOLUTION

$$\text{percent of change} = \frac{\text{amount of change}}{\text{original amount}} \cdot 100\%$$

$$= \frac{150 - 125}{125} \cdot 100\%$$

$$= \frac{25}{125} \cdot 100\%$$

$$= 0.2 \cdot 100\%$$

$$= 20\%$$

The percent increase was 20%.

B Juan bought a new car for $16,000. A year later, its value was $13,600. What was the percent decrease in the value of the car in 1 year?

SOLUTION

$$\text{percent of change} = \frac{\text{amount of change}}{\text{original amount}} \cdot 100\%$$

$$= \frac{13,600 - 16,000}{16,000} \cdot 100\%$$

$$= \frac{-2400}{16,000} \cdot 100\%$$

$$= -0.15 \cdot 100\%$$

$$= -15\%$$

The percent decrease was 15%. ■

Using Percent Increase and Decrease

You can use a known percent of change to find a new value.

EXAMPLE 3

A A worker's salary is increased by 5%. If the old salary was $12,500/year, what is the worker's new salary?

SOLUTION

Find the amount of increase, and then add that amount to the original amount.

increase = 5% of 12,500   Find the increase.

$\quad\quad -0.05 \times 12,500$

$\quad\quad = 625$

original amount + increase = new amount   Find the new amount.

$12,500 + 625 = 13,125$ Add the increase to the original amount.

The worker's new salary is $13,125.

B Nathan weighed 180 lb. He went on a diet and lost 10% of his weight. What was Nathan's new weight?

SOLUTION

Find the amount of decrease, and then subtract this amount from the original amount.

decrease = 10% of 180   Find the decrease.

$\quad\quad = 0.10 \times 180$

$\quad\quad = 18$

original amount − decrease = new amount   Find the new amount.

$180 - 18 = 162$ Subtract the decrease from the original amount.

Nathan's new weight was 162 lb. ■

Application: Zoology

Camels can go for a week without drinking water. A camel can survive a 40% weight loss due to lack of water. If a camel starts off weighing 1200 lb, how much will the camel weigh after a 40% weight loss?

SOLUTION

decrease = 40% of 1200   Find the decrease.

$\quad\quad\quad = 0.40 \times 1200$

$\quad\quad\quad = 480$

original amount − decrease = new amount   Find the new amount.

$1200 - 480 = 720$ Subtract the decrease from the original amount.

After a 40% weight loss, a camel originally weighing 1200 lb would weigh 720 lb. ■

Application: Real Estate

EXAMPLE 5

Mariah's house has appreciated in value over the last 3 years. It has gone from being worth $125,000 to being worth $175,000. What is the percent increase in the value of Mariah's house?

SOLUTION

$$\text{percent of change} = \frac{\text{amount of change}}{\text{original amount}} \cdot 100\%$$

$$= \frac{175,000 - 125,000}{125,000} \cdot 100\%$$

$$= \frac{50,000}{125,000} \cdot 100\%$$

$$= 0.4 \cdot 100\%$$

$$= 40\%$$

There has been a 40% increase in the value of Mariah's house. ∎

Application: Sports

EXAMPLE 6

A The chart shows Nathan's bowling scores. What was the percent increase in his score from Game 1 to Game 2?

Game	Score
1	180
2	200
3	180

SOLUTION

$$\text{percent of change} = \frac{\text{amount of change}}{\text{original amount}} \cdot 100\%$$

$$= \frac{200 - 180}{180} \cdot 100\%$$

$$= \frac{20}{180} \cdot 100\%$$

$$\approx 0.11 \cdot 100\%$$

$$\approx 11\%$$

Nathan's score increased about 11% from Game 1 to Game 2.

B What was the percent decrease in Nathan's score from Game 2 to Game 3?

SOLUTION

$$\text{percent of change} = \frac{\text{amount of change}}{\text{original amount}} \cdot 100\%$$

$$= \frac{180 - 200}{200} \cdot 100\%$$

$$= \frac{-20}{200} \cdot 100\%$$

$$= -0.1 \cdot 100\%$$

$$= -10\%$$

Nathan's score decreased 10% from Game 2 to Game 3. ▪

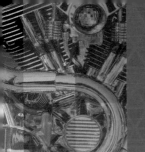

Percent Error

The **percent error** of a quantity's measurement indicates how close the measurement is to the quantity's actual value.

Calculating Percent Error

Percent Error Formula

$$\text{percent error} = \frac{|\text{measured value} - \text{actual value}|}{\text{actual value}} \cdot 100\%$$

EXAMPLE 1

The measured width of a small bookcase is 90.6 cm. Its actual width is 90 cm. Find the percent error of the measurement. Round your answer to the nearest tenth of a percent.

▶ **Think About It** The absolute value of the difference between the measured value and the actual value is known as the **absolute error**.

SOLUTION

Use the percent error formula to calculate the percent error of the measured value.

$$\frac{|90.6 - 90|}{90} \cdot 100\% = \frac{|0.6|}{90} \cdot 100\% = \left(\frac{0.6}{90} \cdot 100\right)\% = \left(\frac{60}{90}\right)\% \approx 0.7\%$$

The percent error in the measured value is about 0.7%. ■

Calculating Percent Error in an Estimate

Calculate the percent error in an estimate by substituting the estimated value in the percent error formula for the measured value. Then calculate the percent error as you would normally.

> ▶ **Think About It** Percent error is always greater than or equal to 0%. Its value is never negative.

EXAMPLE 2

Gunther estimates a mountain is 3000 m high. He later learns its actual height is 2876 m. What is the percent error in his estimate? Round your answer to the nearest tenth of a percent.

SOLUTION

Substitute the estimated and actual values into the percent error formula, and then calculate the percent error.

$$\frac{|2876 - 3000|}{2876} \cdot 100\% = \frac{|-124|}{2876} \cdot 100\% = \left(\frac{124}{2876} \cdot 100\right)\%$$

$$= \frac{12{,}400}{2876}\% \approx 4.3\%$$

The percent error in the estimated value is about 4.3%. ■

EXAMPLE 3

A scale is 10% off in measuring mass. The actual mass of a bracelet is 30 g. What masses might the scale show?

SOLUTION

Substitute known values into the percent error formula, and then solve for the bracelet's measured mass. The percent error is 10%, and the actual mass is 30 g. Let m represent the measured mass.

$$\frac{|\text{measured mass} - \text{actual mass}|}{\text{actual mass}} \cdot 100\% = \text{percent error}$$

$$\frac{|m - 30|}{30} \cdot 100\% = 10\%$$

$$\frac{|m - 30|}{30} \cdot \frac{100\%}{100\%} = \frac{10\%}{100\%}$$

$$\frac{|m - 30|}{30} = 0.1$$

$$30 \cdot \frac{|m - 30|}{30} = 30 \cdot 0.1$$

$$|m - 30| = 3$$

The equation $|m - 30| = 3$ is a distance equation indicating that the distance between m and 30 is 3. There are two values that are a distance of 3 units from 30: 27 and 33.

The scale is likely to show that the bracelet's mass is between 27 g and 33 g. ■

Multistep Ratio and Percent Problems

It often takes several steps to solve a real-world percent problem.

Application: Percent of Total Cost

Some real-world problems involve finding the percent that an individual cost is of the total cost. To find the percent of a total cost, first add all of the individual costs to find the total cost. Then find the ratio of the individual cost to the total cost and multiply this ratio by 100%.

Percent of Total Cost

$$\text{percent of total cost} = \frac{\text{individual cost}}{\text{total cost}} \cdot 100\%$$

EXAMPLE 1

Membership at a health club costs $35/month plus a one-time initial fee of $50. For a 1-year membership, what percent of the total cost is the initial fee? Round your answer to the nearest tenth of a percent.

▶ **Think About It** Many contracts for a monthly service, such as for a cell phone or a club membership, include a one-time initial fee as well as a monthly charge.

SOLUTION

The total cost is the sum of the initial fee and the total monthly charges.
The total monthly charges equal the product of the monthly fee and 12, the
number of months in 1 year.

$$\$50 + \$35 \cdot 12 = \$50 + \$420 = \$470$$

Find the percent that the initial fee is of the total cost.

$$\frac{\$50}{\$470} \cdot 100\% \approx 10.6\%$$

The initial fee is about 10.6% of the total cost for 1 year. ■

Application: Pre-Tax Price from a Final Price

Final Price Formula
The final price of an item is the sum of the pre-tax price and the amount of tax on the item. final price = pre-tax price + tax paid

The tax paid is often a percent of the item's pre-tax price. You find the
tax paid by converting the tax rate, expressed as a percent, to a decimal.
Then multiply the decimal by the pre-tax price to find the tax paid.

▶ **Think About It** The sales tax rate changes from state to state and,
in some cases, from county to county within a state.

EXAMPLE 2

Jenn bought a sweater for $41.73. The price she paid included 7% sales tax. What was the price of the sweater before the tax was added?

> ▶ **Remember** The amount of tax paid is the product of the sales tax rate, as a decimal, and the pre-tax price.

SOLUTION

The price Jenn paid for the sweater is equal to the sum of the price before tax and the amount of tax paid. Let p be the pre-tax price. The tax paid is 7% of the pre-tax price, represented by $0.07p$.

$$\text{final price} = \text{pre-tax price} + \text{tax paid}$$
$$41.73 = p + 0.07p$$
$$41.73 = 1.07p$$
$$\frac{41.73}{1.07} = \frac{1.07p}{1.07}$$
$$39 = p$$

The price of the sweater before the tax was $39. ▪

Simple Interest

If you borrow money from a bank, you have to pay interest. But if you deposit money into a savings account, the bank will pay you interest.

Interest is the cost to borrow money. **Principal** is money that earns interest at a given rate over time. The **interest rate** is the percentage of the original amount of money that the interest is based on. **Simple interest** is interest earned at a fixed percent of the initial deposit, or principal amount.

Simple Interest Formula

When principal P is invested at annual interest rate r for t years, then the simple interest I earned is

$$I = Prt.$$

Borrowing Money

EXAMPLE 1

A Laura borrowed $48,000 at a 6% interest rate for 7 years. What was the total interest?

SOLUTION

$I = Prt$

$\quad = \$48,000 \cdot 0.06 \cdot 7$ Substitute.

$\quad = \$20,160$ Multiply.

The total interest was $20,160.

B Bryan borrowed $12,800 at a 4.8% interest rate for 6 years. What was the total interest?

SOLUTION

$I = Prt$

$= \$12,800 \cdot 0.048 \cdot 6$ Substitute.

$= \$3686.40$ Multiply.

The total interest was $3686.40. ▪

▶ **Remember** To write a percent as a decimal, move the decimal point two places to the left.

Saving Money

EXAMPLE 2

Cecil deposited $5600 in a savings account earning 2.5% interest over 8 years. What was the total interest earned after 8 years?

SOLUTION

$I = Prt$

$= \$5600 \cdot 0.025 \cdot 8$ Substitute.

$= \$1120$ Multiply.

Cecil's account earned $1120 in interest. ▪

Using the Simple Interest Formula to Calculate Other Values

EXAMPLE 3

A Fritz borrowed $8000 at an interest rate of 6%. He paid $1440 interest. Fritz borrowed the money for how much time?

SOLUTION

$$I = Prt$$

$\$1400 = \$8000 \cdot 0.06 \cdot t$ Substitute.

$\$1440 = \$480t$ Multiply.

$\dfrac{\$1440}{\$480} = \dfrac{\$480t}{\$480}$ Divide each side by $480.

$3 = t$

Fritz borrowed the money for 3 years.

B Hillary borrowed $1500 for 5 years. She paid $435 in interest. What was the interest rate?

SOLUTION

$$I = Prt$$

$\$435 = \$1500 \cdot r \cdot 5$ Substitute.

$\$435 = \$7500r$ Multiply.

$\dfrac{\$435}{\$7500} = \dfrac{\$7500r}{\$7500}$ Divide each side by $7500.

$0.058 = r$

$5.8\% = r$

The interest rate was 5.8%.

C Sue earned $99.75 in interest from her savings account. If the interest rate is 2.5% over 7 years, what amount did Sue deposit?

SOLUTION

$$I = Prt$$

$\$99.75 = P \cdot 0.025 \cdot 7$ Substitute and solve for P.

$\$99.75 = 0.175P$ Multiply.

$\dfrac{\$99.75}{0.175} = \dfrac{0.175P}{0.175}$ Divide each side by 0.175.

$\$570 = P$

Sue deposited $570. ▪

Proportions

Model builders use proportions to figure out the length of every item in their models. For the model to be accurate, every length needs to be in the same proportion to the original object.

Proportion

Ratios that describe the same numerical relationship are **equivalent ratios**.

Finding Equivalent Ratios

Multiplying or dividing the numerator and the denominator of a fraction by the same value is the same as multiplying the fraction by a form of 1. Multiplying by 1 does not change the value, so it's a good way to find equivalent ratios.

▶ **Think About It** Saying that a ratio is $\frac{1.5}{2}$ is okay, but for convenience, generally try to use integer values for the numerator and denominator and write the ratio as $\frac{3}{4}$.

EXAMPLE 1

Find two ratios that are equivalent to the given ratio.

A $20 : 25$

SOLUTION

Write the ratio as a fraction. Then multiply or divide the numerator and the denominator by the same nonzero number.

$$\frac{20}{25} = \frac{20 \div 5}{25 \div 5} = \frac{4}{5}$$

$$\frac{20}{25} = \frac{20 \cdot 3}{25 \cdot 3} = \frac{60}{75}$$

B $3:4$

SOLUTION

This ratio is already in simplest form, so you can only multiply the numerator and the denominator by the same nonzero number.

$$\frac{3}{4} = \frac{3 \cdot 2}{4 \cdot 2} = \frac{6}{8}$$

$$\frac{3}{4} = \frac{3 \cdot 10}{4 \cdot 10} = \frac{30}{40} \quad \blacksquare$$

▶ **Think About It** Any given ratio has infinite equivalent ratios because there are infinite versions of 1 to multiply by.

Determining Whether Ratios Are Proportional

A **proportion** is an equation stating that two ratios are equal. In the proportion $\frac{a}{b} = \frac{c}{d}$, a and d are called the **extremes** and b and c are called the **means**. These definitions are easier to remember when you write the proportion with colons, because the extremes are on the exterior and the means are in the middle.

$$a : b = c : d$$

▶ **Think About It** Read the proportion $\frac{a}{b} = \frac{c}{d}$ as "a is to b as c is to d."

Two ratios form a proportion if and only if the product of the means is equal to the product of the extremes.

Means-Extremes Product Property

For any a and c and nonzero b and d, $\dfrac{a}{b} = \dfrac{c}{d}$ if and only if $ad = bc$.

Example

$\dfrac{3}{5} = \dfrac{9}{15}$ because $3 \cdot 15 = 5 \cdot 9$

$\dfrac{7}{10} \neq \dfrac{2}{3}$ because $7 \cdot 3 \neq 10 \cdot 2$

If two ratios form a proportion, those ratios are called proportional, or in proportion.

When you write the product of the means and the product of the extremes, it is sometimes called **cross multiplying**.

ad is the product of the extremes.
bc is the product of the means.

ad and bc are called cross products.

You could also simplify each ratio to determine whether they are proportional, but cross multiplying is generally quicker.

▶ **Think About It** These all mean the same thing:

- equal ratios
- equivalent ratios
- proportional ratios
- ratios in proportion

EXAMPLE 2

Determine whether the ratios are proportional.

A $\dfrac{4}{6}$ and $\dfrac{10}{15}$

SOLUTION

Method 1 Use the means-extremes product property.

$$4 \cdot 15 \overset{?}{=} 6 \cdot 10$$
$$60 = 60$$

The cross products are equal, so $\dfrac{4}{6}$ and $\dfrac{10}{15}$ are proportional.

Method 2 Simplify the ratios and then compare them.

$$\frac{4}{6} = \frac{4 \div 2}{6 \div 2} = \frac{2}{3}$$

$$\frac{10}{15} = \frac{10 \div 5}{15 \div 5} = \frac{2}{3}$$

The simplified ratios are identical, so $\dfrac{4}{6}$ and $\dfrac{10}{15}$ are proportional.

B $\dfrac{8}{12}$ and $\dfrac{24}{30}$

SOLUTION

Method 1 Use the means-extremes product property.

$$8 \cdot 30 \overset{?}{=} 12 \cdot 24$$
$$240 \neq 288$$

The products are not equal, so $\dfrac{8}{12}$ and $\dfrac{24}{30}$ are not proportional.

Method 2 Simplify the ratios and then compare them.

$$\frac{8}{12} = \frac{8 \div 4}{12 \div 4} = \frac{2}{3}$$

$$\frac{24}{30} = \frac{24 \div 6}{30 \div 6} = \frac{4}{5}$$

The simplified ratios are not identical, so $\dfrac{8}{12}$ and $\dfrac{24}{30}$ are not proportional. ∎

Solving Proportions

You can use the means-extremes product property to solve proportions.

EXAMPLE 3

Solve the proportion.

A $\dfrac{n}{15} = \dfrac{6}{20}$

SOLUTION

$$\dfrac{n}{15} = \dfrac{6}{20}$$

$20n = 6 \cdot 15$ Multiply means and extremes (cross multiply).

$20n = 90$ Multiply.

$\dfrac{20n}{20} = \dfrac{90}{20}$ Divide each side by 20.

$n = 4.5$

B $\dfrac{5.6}{14} = \dfrac{x}{8}$

SOLUTION

$$\dfrac{5.6}{14} = \dfrac{x}{8}$$

$8 \cdot 5.6 = 14x$ Multiply means and extremes (cross multiply).

$44.8 = 14x$ Multiply.

$\dfrac{44.8}{14} = \dfrac{14x}{14}$ Divide each side by 14.

$3.2 = x$ ■

Application: Travel

You can apply proportions to many real-world situations.

EXAMPLE 4

A train traveled 234 mi in 4 h. If the train continues at the same rate, how many miles will it travel in 10 h?

> ▶ **Think About It** When you set up a proportion, include the units so that you can see whether you have put everything in the right place.

SOLUTION

Write and solve a proportion.

$\dfrac{234 \text{ mi}}{4 \text{ h}} = \dfrac{x \text{ miles}}{10 \text{ h}}$ The train continues at the same rate, so the rate for 4 h equals the rate for 10 h.

$\dfrac{234}{4} = \dfrac{x}{10}$ Write the proportion without units.

$2340 = 4x$ Cross multiply.

$\dfrac{2340}{4} = \dfrac{4x}{4}$ Divide both sides by 4.

$585 = x$ Simplify.

The train will travel 585 mi in 10 h. ■

> ▶ **Think About It** In Example 4, the proportion could have been set up as $\dfrac{4 \text{ h}}{234 \text{ mi}} = \dfrac{10 \text{ h}}{x \text{ miles}}$.

Proportional Relationships

You can use equations and tables to describe proportional relationships.

Definitions

A relationship between x and y is a **proportional relationship** if you can write the relationship between the two variables in a form of the **general equation**, $y = kx$, where k is the **constant of variation**.

Identifying Proportional Relationships and the Constant of Variation

If $y = kx$, then $k = \dfrac{y}{x}$. If $\dfrac{y}{x}$ is the same value k for every ordered pair (x, y), then x and y have a proportional relationship.

EXAMPLE 1

Determine whether the relationship is proportional. If so, state the constant of variation.

 A

x	2	4	6	8	10
y	5	10	15	20	25

SOLUTION

Divide each value of y by its corresponding x-value.

$$\frac{5}{2} = 2.5, \frac{10}{4} = 2.5, \frac{15}{6} = 2.5, \frac{20}{8} = 2.5, \frac{25}{10} = 2.5$$

The relationship is proportional with a constant of variation of 2.5.

B $y - 4 = -2x$

SOLUTION

Solve for y to see if the specific equation fits the form of the general equation $y = kx$.

$y - 4 = -2x$

$\quad y = -2x + 4 \qquad$ Add 4 to each side.

The equation does not fit the form of the general equation because it has a constant term 4. The relationship is not proportional. ■

Writing and Using Equations for Proportional Relationships

You can write an equation for a proportional relationship if you know a pair of values.

EXAMPLE 2

If y and x have a proportional relationship, and $y = -12$ when $x = 18$, find the value of y when $x = 15$.

SOLUTION

Step 1 Find k.

$y = kx \qquad\qquad$ General form of equation

$k = \dfrac{y}{x} \qquad\qquad$ Solve the general equation for k.

$k = \dfrac{-12}{18} \qquad\quad$ Substitute -12 for y and 18 for x.

$k = -\dfrac{2}{3} \qquad\quad$ Simplify.

Step 2 Substitute the value of k found in Step 1 into the general equation.

$y = kx$ — General form of equation

$y = -\frac{2}{3}x$ — Substitute $-\frac{2}{3}$ for k to obtain the specific equation.

Step 3 Use the specific equation $y = -\frac{2}{3}x$ to find y when $x = 15$.

$y = -\frac{2}{3}x$ — Specific equation

$\quad = -\frac{2}{3} \cdot 15$ — Substitute 15 for x.

$\quad = -10$ — Simplify.

So $y = -10$ when $x = 15$. ■

> ▶ **Think About It** The equation for a proportional relationship is $y = kx$. Once you find the constant of variation and substitute that value for k in the general equation, you get the specific equation for a particular problem.

Application: Cost

EXAMPLE 3

The cost of grapes is proportional to the weight. If 3.5 lb of grapes costs $4.55, write an equation that represents the relationship. Then determine the number of pounds of grapes that can be purchased for $10.14, before tax.

SOLUTION

Step 1 Find the equation. Let w represent the weight and c represent the cost.

The cost is proportional to the number of pounds, so $c = 4.55$ when $w = 3.5$. Find k.

$$k = \frac{c}{w} = \frac{4.55}{3.5} = 1.3$$

The specific equation is $c = 1.3w$.

Step 2 Substitute 10.14 for c and solve for w.

$c = 1.3w$

10.14 $= 1.3w$ Substitute 10.14 for c.

$7.8 = w$ Divide each side by 1.3.

So 7.8 lb of grapes can be purchased for $10.14, before tax. ▪

Graphing Proportions

You can use the graph of a proportional relationship to find the ratio of the two quantities.

Rates

Each point on the graph of a proportional relationship represents a rate. You can find the rate by calculating the ratio of the *y*-coordinate to the *x*-coordinate.

▶ **Remember** A rate is a ratio of two quantities measured in different units.

EXAMPLE 1

The number of loaves of bread baked is proportional to the amount of sugar used. The graph shows this relationship.

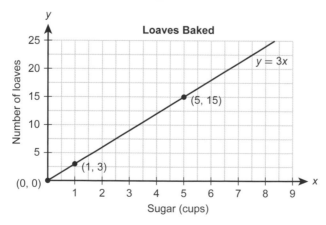

A What rate does the point $(5, 15)$ on the graph represent?

SOLUTION

The x-coordinate represents 5 cups of sugar, and the y-coordinate represents 15 loaves baked. So the ratio of loaves of bread baked to sugar used is $\frac{y}{x}$, equal to the rate of $\frac{15 \text{ loaves}}{5 \text{ cups}}$.

B What does the point $(0, 0)$ represent?

SOLUTION

The x-coordinate represents 0 cups of sugar, and the y-coordinate represents 0 loaves baked. So for every 0 cups of sugar used, 0 loaves of bread are baked.

The point $(0, 0)$ does **not** represent a rate, since the ratio of loaves baked to sugar used is $\frac{0}{0}$, which is undefined because the denominator is 0.

C Why does the point $(1, 3)$ represent a unit rate?

SOLUTION

The x-coordinate represents 1 cup of sugar, and the y-coordinate represents 3 loaves baked. Thus, the ratio of loaves of bread baked to sugar used is $\frac{y}{x}$, equal to the rate of $\frac{3 \text{ loaves}}{1 \text{ cup}}$, which is the unit rate of 3 loaves/cup. ■

EXAMPLE 2

The graph shows the price of silver in relation to the amount of silver purchased.

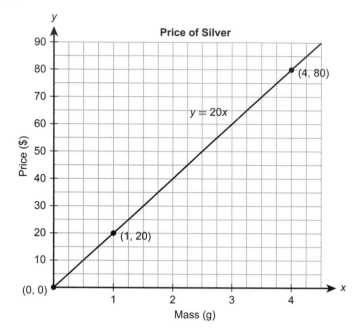

▶ **Think About It** The price of precious metals such as silver is often given in dollars per gram.

A How does the point $(4, 80)$ represent a rate?

SOLUTION

The x-coordinate represents a mass of 4 g, and the y-coordinate represents a price of \$80. The ratio of the price of silver to the amount purchased is $\dfrac{y}{x}$, equal to the rate $\dfrac{\$80}{4 \text{ g}}$.

Q According to the graph, how much would 2 g of silver cost?

A $40

B How does the point $(1, 20)$ represent a unit rate?

SOLUTION

The x-coordinate represents a mass of 1 g, and the y-coordinate represents a price of $20. The ratio of the price of silver to the amount purchased is $\frac{y}{x}$, equal to the unit rate of $20/g.

C Explain why the points $(4, 80)$ and $(1, 20)$ show that the price of silver varies directly with the amount purchased.

SOLUTION

For both points, the ratio of $\frac{y}{x}$ is equal to 20.

$$\text{point }(4, 80): \frac{80}{4} - 20$$

$$\text{point }(1, 20): \frac{20}{1} = 20$$

Because the ratio of y to x is constant, at 20, the price of silver varies directly with the amount purchased, with a constant of variation of $20. ▪

Constant of Proportionality

You can determine the constant of proportionality between two quantities from a table of values, an equation, or a graph.

Finding the Constant of Proportionality

Definitions

Two quantities that vary directly with each other are also said to be **directly proportional.**

The **constant of proportionality** is equal to the ratio of the two directly proportional quantities.

You find the constant of proportionality k between two proportional quantities x and y as you would find the constant of variation between two quantities that vary directly with each other. Find the ratio between the quantities: $k = \dfrac{y}{x}$.

▶ **Think About It** The constant of proportionality is just another term for the constant of variation.

EXAMPLE

Tami makes salsa at a restaurant. The amount of salsa made is proportional to the amount of lime juice used.

Lime juice (tbsp)	2	4	6
Salsa (cups)	5	10	15

A Find the constant of proportionality.

SOLUTION

The constant of proportionality is the ratio of the amount of salsa made to the amount of lime juice used.

$$\frac{5}{2} = 2.5, \frac{10}{4} = 2.5, \frac{15}{6} = 2.5$$

The constant of proportionality is 2.5.

B Write an equation expressing the relationship between the two quantities. Graph the equation along with the values from the table.

SOLUTION

Let S be the amount of salsa made and L be the amount of lime juice used.

If $\frac{S}{L} = 2.5$, then $S = 2.5L$.

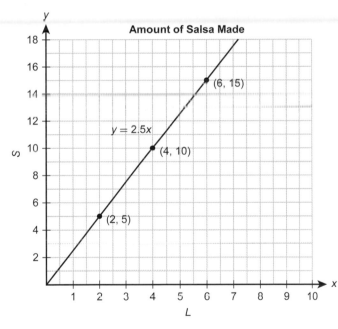

Expressions and Inequalities

Solving equations requires balance. Anything you do that changes the value of one side of the equation has to be done to the other side. Keep your equations balanced and you'll have a rock-solid foundation.

Like Terms

To simplify some variable expressions, you need to identify and combine like terms.

Identifying Like Terms

A sum or difference expression is made up of terms. **Like terms** have the same variable part or parts. Numbers are considered to be like terms; they can be called numerical terms. Terms are made up of factors that are multiplied together.

> ▶ **Think About It** Like terms can have exponents. For example, the like terms $3x^2$ and $5x^2$ have the exponent 2.

EXAMPLE 1

Identify the like terms.

A $5x, 5y, -2x, 5, -11$

SOLUTION

$\{5x, -2x\}, \{5, -11\}, 5y$ The terms $5x$ and $-2x$ have the same variable.
The terms 5 and -11 are numerical terms.

The terms $5x$ and $-2x$ form one pair of like terms, and the terms 5 and -11 form another pair of like terms.

B $-3a, 2b, 6ab, 1, a$

SOLUTION

The term $6ab$ is the only term that has both variables a and b, so it is not like any of the other terms.

$\{-3a, a\}, 2b, 6ab, 1$ The terms $-3a$ and a have the same variable.

The terms $-3a$ and a are like terms.

C $6, 4p, 6p^2, -p, 3pq$

SOLUTION

$6, \{4p, -p\}, 6p^2, 3pq$ The terms $4p$ and $-p$ have the same variables.

The terms $4p$ and $-p$ are like terms. ■

Using the Distributive Property to Combine Like Terms

The distributive property states that $a(b + c) = ab + ac$, which can also be written $ba + ca = (b + c)a$. If you have an expression like $5x - 2x$, you can use the distributive property to write it as $(5 - 2)x$ and simplify it to $3x$ to combine like terms.

EXAMPLE 2

Combine like terms.

A $5x + 2x$

SOLUTION

$5x + 2x = (5 + 2)x$ Apply the distributive property $ba + ca = (b + c)a$.

$ = 7x$ Add inside the parentheses.

B $3y - y + 6y$

SOLUTION

$$3y - y + 6y = 3y - 1y + 6y \qquad \text{Write } -y \text{ as } -1y \text{ so that it has a numerical factor.}$$

$$= (3 - 1 + 6)y \qquad \text{Apply the distributive property.}$$

$$= 8y \qquad \text{Simplify inside the parentheses.} \ \blacksquare$$

Identifying and Combining Like Terms

The numerical factor in a term is called a **coefficient**. To combine like terms, you only need to add or subtract the coefficients.

Combining Like Terms

To combine like terms, combine their coefficients. Keep the variable part the same.

Examples $4x + 5x = 9x$

$$3ab + 2ab - 1ab = 4ab$$

▶ **Remember** Combining like terms is based on the distributive property.

$$4x + 5x = (4 + 5)x = 9x$$

EXAMPLE 3

Combine the like terms in the expression.

A $2a + 3 - 5a + 8b + 3ab$

SOLUTION

$$2a + 3 - 5a + 8b + 3ab = \mathbf{2a - 5a} + 3 + 8b + 3ab \qquad \text{Rewrite so that like terms are together.}$$

$$= \mathbf{-3a} + 3 + 8b + 3ab \qquad \text{Combine like terms.}$$

B $3s + rs - 4r - 6rs - 8rs$

SOLUTION

$$3s + \mathbf{rs} - 4r - \mathbf{6rs} - \mathbf{8rs} = 3s - 4r + \mathbf{1rs} - \mathbf{6rs} - \mathbf{8rs} \qquad \text{Rewrite } rs \text{ as } 1rs. \text{ Write like terms together.}$$

$$= 3s - 4r - 13rs \qquad \text{Combine like terms.} \ \blacksquare$$

Application: Sales Tax

EXAMPLE 4

The sales tax rate in a certain state is 5%. Write a simplified expression for the total cost of an item that has a price of x dollars.

SOLUTION

The decimal equivalent of 5% is 0.05. When you pay 5% of x dollars in sales tax, you pay $0.05x$ dollars in sales tax.

$$\text{total cost} = \underbrace{\text{price of item}} + \underbrace{\text{sales tax}}$$

$$= \quad x \quad + \quad 0.05x$$

$$= \quad 1.00x \quad + \quad 0.05x \qquad \text{Write } x \text{ as } 1.00x.$$

$$= \quad 1.05x \qquad \text{Combine like terms.}$$

The total amount paid is $1.05x$ dollars. $\blacksquare$

Variable Expressions

Identifying and combining like terms in a math expression helps organize the expression and can make evaluating the expression easier.

Identifying Like Terms

Identify like terms in an expression by finding terms with the same variables and exponents. Start at the left of the expression with the first term, looking for terms similar to it. Continue with each term until all terms have been examined.

▶ **Remember** Two terms in an expression are like terms if the terms have the same variables and the same exponents on those variables.

EXAMPLE 1

On her pre-algebra test, Lin Yi was asked to identify all of the like terms from the list.

$$5xy, -2x, \frac{1}{3}, 0.6x, 2y, 8$$

She answered the question by identifying $-2x$ and $0.6x$ as like terms.

A Are the terms $-2x$ and $0.6x$ like terms? Explain.

SOLUTION
The terms $-2x$ and $0.6x$ are like terms. They have the same variable, x, raised to the same power, 1.

B Identify any other like terms. Explain how the terms are alike.

SOLUTION

The terms $\frac{1}{3}$ and 8 are constants, so they are considered to be like terms.

No other terms are alike. ▪

Combining Like Terms

The solution to certain real-world problems involves adding variable expressions. To find the solution, it helps to combine like terms.

EXAMPLE 2

Mia and Jeff plan to meet at the library. The figure details the path and distance (in kilometers) each of them walks to get to the library.

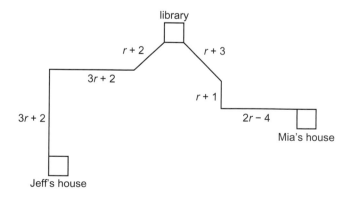

A How far did Mia walk?

SOLUTION

$$(2r - 4) + (r + 1) + (r + 3) = 2r + r + r - 4 + 1 + 3$$
$$= 4r$$

Mia walked $4r$ kilometers.

B How far did Jeff walk?

SOLUTION

$$2(3r + 2) + (r + 2) = 6r + 4 + r + 2$$
$$= 6r + r + 4 + 2$$
$$= 7r + 6$$

Jeff walked $7r + 6$ kilometers.

C If r is positive, then Jeff walked farther than Mia did. How much farther did he walk?

SOLUTION

$$7r + 6 - 4r = 7r - 4r + 6$$
$$= 3r + 6$$

Jeff walked $3r + 6$ kilometers farther than Mia. ■

Adding and Subtracting Linear Expressions

You can use the properties of numbers when adding and subtracting like terms in linear expressions.

> ▶ **Remember** When you combine like terms in a linear expression that contains subtraction, make sure the subtraction sign is kept in front of the term being subtracted.
>
> $$3x - 4 - 2x + 3 = (3x - 2x) + (-4 + 3)$$

EXAMPLE 3

Determine whether to add or subtract the linear expressions. Then simplify.

A Find the perimeter of the polygon.

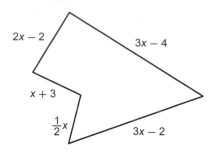

SOLUTION

The perimeter of a polygon is the total length of all its sides. So add the expressions and simplify.

$$(2x - 2) + (3x - 4) + (x + 3) + \frac{1}{2}x + (3x - 2) = 2x + 3x + x + \frac{1}{2}x + 3x - 2 - 4 + 3 - 2$$
$$= 9\frac{1}{2}x - 5$$

The perimeter of the polygon is $9\frac{1}{2}x - 5$ units.

B Melanie and Todd are raising money for a children's hospital. Melanie will earn $1.5x + 49.50$ dollars after swimming x laps, and Todd will earn $0.75x + 35$ dollars after swimming x laps. How much more money will Melanie earn than Todd if they both swim the same number of laps?

SOLUTION

To find how much more Melanie will earn than Todd, find the difference between the two expressions and simplify.

$$1.5x + 49.50 - (0.75x + 35) = 1.5x - 0.75x + 49.50 - 35$$
$$= 0.75x + 14.50$$

Melanie will earn $0.75x + 14.50$ dollars more than Todd if they swim the same number of laps. ■

Equivalent Expressions

Two expressions can be written in different forms and still have the same value. These expressions are called **equivalent expressions**. You can determine whether two expressions are equivalent by using the properties of equality to rewrite one of the expressions in the same form as the other expression. The expressions can then be compared to determine whether they are equivalent.

EXAMPLE 4

Determine whether the expressions are equivalent.

A $-4 + 3x$ and $\frac{1}{2}(6x - 8)$

SOLUTION

$$\frac{1}{2}(6x - 8) = 3x - 4 \qquad \text{Apply the distributive property.}$$
$$= -4 + 3x \qquad \text{Apply the commutative property.}$$

The expressions $-4 + 3x$ and $\frac{1}{2}(6x - 8)$ are equivalent.

B $5 - 4(1.5 - x)$ and $1.5 - x$

SOLUTION

$$5 - 4(1.5 - x) = 5 - 6 + 4x \qquad \text{Apply the distributive property.}$$
$$= -1 + 4x \qquad \text{Add.}$$

The expressions $5 - 4(1.5 - x)$ and $1.5 - x$ are not equivalent. ∎

> ▶ **Think About It** You can determine that these two expressions are not equivalent without rewriting one of them. One expression is the quantity $1.5 - x$. The other expression multiplies this quantity by 4 and then subtracts the product from 5. Therefore, the expression $1.5 - x$ cannot be equivalent to the other expression.

Equations Involving Addition and Subtraction

To solve equations, you need to understand equivalent equations.

Equivalent equations are equations with the same solution or solutions. Related equations are equivalent, but you can also use properties of equality to create equivalent equations.

Properties of Equality

Property	Example
Addition Property of Equality If you add the same number to both sides of an equation, you obtain an equivalent equation.	
If $a = b$, then $a + c = b + c$ and $c + a = c + b$.	If $n = 3$, then $n + \mathbf{2} = 3 + \mathbf{2}$. If $x - 4 = 9$, then $x - 4 + \mathbf{4} = 9 + \mathbf{4}$.
Subtraction Property of Equality If you subtract the same number from both sides of an equation, you obtain an equivalent equation.	
If $a = b$, then $a - c = b - c$.	If $r = 7$, then $r - \mathbf{5} = 7 - \mathbf{5}$. If $x + 3 = 12$, then $x + 3 - \mathbf{3} = 12 - \mathbf{3}$.
Substitution Property of Equality A value or expression may replace an equal value or expression.	
If $a = b$, then either may replace the other in any expression.	If $x = 6$, then you can rewrite the expression $x - 10$ as $\mathbf{6} - 10$.

Solving Addition and Subtraction Equations

Addition and subtraction are inverse operations. To solve an equation, use inverse operations to obtain one or more simpler equations that are equivalent. When you obtain the simplest equivalent equation, you have the solution.

How to Solve Addition and Subtraction Equations

If a number is subtracted from a variable in an equation, add that same number to both sides of the equation to undo the subtraction.

If a number is added to a variable in an equation, subtract that same number from both sides of the equation to undo the addition.

EXAMPLE 1

Solve the equation. Check your answer.

A $x - 10 = -4$

SOLUTION

$$x - 10 = -4$$

$$x - 10 + \mathbf{10} = -4 + \mathbf{10} \qquad \text{To undo the subtraction, add 10 to both sides.}$$

$$x + 0 = 6 \qquad \text{Opposites sum to zero.}$$

$$x = 6$$

▶ **Think About It** We often don't show the step $x + 0 = 6$, but it's always implied.

CHECK

$$x - 10 = -4$$

$$\mathbf{6} - 10 \stackrel{?}{=} -4 \qquad \text{Substitute 6 for } x.$$

$$-4 = -4 \checkmark$$

The answer is correct.

▶ **Think About It** The equations

$$x - 10 = -4,$$

$$x - 10 + 10 = -4 + 10,$$

and

$$x = 6$$

are all equivalent equations. The solution is given by the simplest equation,

$$x = 6.$$

B $x + 15 = -10$

SOLUTION

$$x + 15 = -10$$

$$x + 15 - \mathbf{15} = -10 - \mathbf{15} \qquad \text{To undo the addition, subtract 15 from both sides.}$$

$$x = -25$$

CHECK

$$x + 15 = -10$$

$$-\mathbf{25} + 15 \overset{?}{=} -10 \qquad \text{Substitute } -25 \text{ for } x.$$

$$-10 = -10 \checkmark$$

The answer is correct. ▪

Solving Equations Involving Decimals

Use the same strategies that you use with integers to solve equations with decimals.

EXAMPLE 2

Solve.

A $x + 5.3 = 15$

SOLUTION

$$x + 5.3 = 15$$

$$x + 5.3 - \mathbf{5.3} = 15 - \mathbf{5.3}$$ Subtract 5.3 from both sides.

$$x = 9.7$$

B $23 = d - 9.5$

SOLUTION

$$23 = d - 9.5$$

$$23 + \mathbf{9.5} = d - 9.5 + \mathbf{9.5}$$ Add 9.5 to both sides.

$$32.5 = d \; \blacksquare$$

> ▶ **Remember** Check your solution by substituting it for the variable. A number is a solution if it makes the equation true.

Simplifying Before Solving

With some equations, it is easier to simplify one side of the equation before you perform an inverse operation.

EXAMPLE 3

Solve the equation.

A $-5.2 + x + 3.8 = 13$

SOLUTION

$$-\mathbf{5.2} + x + \mathbf{3.8} = 13$$

$$x + (-\mathbf{5.2}) + \mathbf{3.8} = 13$$ Use the commutative property to rearrange the addends.

$$x + (-\mathbf{1.4}) = 13$$ Add -5.2 and 3.8 to simplify the left side.

$$x - 1.4 = 13$$

$$x - 1.4 + \mathbf{1.4} = 13 + \mathbf{1.4}$$ Add 1.4 to both sides.

$$x = 14.4$$

B $0 = -9.1 - (d + 3)$

SOLUTION

$$0 = -9.1 - (d + 3)$$

$$0 = -9.1 + \left[-(d + 3)\right] \qquad \text{To subtract } (d + 3), \text{ add its opposite, } -(d + 3).$$

$$0 = -9.1 + (-d) + (-3) \qquad \text{Apply the property of the opposite of a sum.}$$

$$0 = -12.1 + (-d) \qquad \text{Add } -9.1 \text{ and } -3 \text{ to simplify the right side.}$$

$$0 + 12.1 = -12.1 + (-d) + 12.1 \qquad \text{Add 12.1 to both sides.}$$

$$12.1 = -d$$

$$-12.1 = d \qquad \text{If the opposite of } d \text{ equals 12.1, then } d \text{ equals } -12.1. \ \blacksquare$$

Application: Landscape Design

EXAMPLE 4

A landscaper has 20 m of border for a garden. She has planned the lengths of three sides. What length is needed for the fourth side so that she can use the entire border?

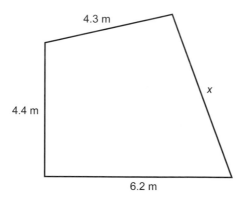

SOLUTION

$$6.2 + 4.4 + 4.3 + x = 20.0$$
$$14.9 + x = 20.0$$
$$14.9 + x - \mathbf{14.9} = 20.0 - \mathbf{14.9}$$
$$x - 14.9 + 14.9 = 20.0 - 14.9$$
$$x = 5.1$$

The length of the fourth side should be 5.1 m. ■

Equations Involving Multiplication and Division

If you divide both sides of an equation by the same nonzero number, the equation will still be true. You can use the division property of equality to solve equations.

Using the Division Property of Equality to Solve Equations

You can use the division property of equality to find equivalent equations. The point of this sort of transformation is to find an equation that makes the solution easy to see.

Division Property of Equality

For a, b, and n $\left(\text{where } n \neq 0\right)$,

If $\quad a = b$,

then $\dfrac{a}{n} = \dfrac{b}{n}$.

Example

If $\quad 2x = 6$

then $\dfrac{2x}{2} = \dfrac{6}{2}$

$\quad\quad x = 3$

All three of these are equivalent equations.

▶ **Remember** Equivalent equations have the same solution.

EXAMPLE 1

Solve.

A $5 \cdot r = -30$

SOLUTION

$5 \cdot r = -30$

$\dfrac{5 \cdot r}{5} = \dfrac{-30}{5}$ Divide both sides of the equation by 5.

$1 \cdot r = -6$ Simplify.

$r = -6$ Identity Property of Multiplication

> ▶ **Think About It** Check your answer by substituting -6 for r in the original equation. The result should be a true equation.
>
> $$5 \cdot r = -30$$
> $$5 \cdot (-6) \overset{?}{=} -30$$
> $$-30 = -30 \checkmark$$

B $2.1 = -7b$

SOLUTION

$2.1 = -7b$

$\dfrac{2.1}{-7} = \dfrac{-7b}{-7}$ Divide both sides of the equation by -7.

$-0.3 = 1 \cdot b$ Simplify.

$-0.3 = b$ Identity Property of Multiplication ■

Using the Multiplication Property of Equality to Solve Equations

If you multiply both sides of an equation by the same number, the equation will still be true. You can use the multiplication property of equality to solve equations.

Multiplication Property of Equality

For a, b, and n,

If $a = b$,

then $an = bn$

Example

If $\dfrac{x}{5} = 3$

then $\dfrac{x}{5} \cdot \mathbf{5} = 3 \cdot \mathbf{5}$

$x = 15$

All three of these are equivalent equations.

EXAMPLE 2

Solve.

A $\dfrac{b}{3} = 10$

SOLUTION

$\dfrac{b}{3} = 10$

$\dfrac{b}{3} \cdot \mathbf{3} = 10 \cdot \mathbf{3}$ Multiply both sides of the equation by 3.

$b \cdot 1 = 30$ Simplify.

$b = 30$ Identity Property of Multiplication

B $3 = \dfrac{w}{0.65}$

SOLUTION

$3 = \dfrac{w}{0.65}$

$3 \cdot \mathbf{0.65} = \dfrac{w}{0.65} \cdot \mathbf{0.65}$ Multiply both sides of the equation by 0.65.

$1.95 = w \cdot 1$ Simplify.

$1.95 = w$ Identity Property of Multiplication ■

Using the Reciprocal to Solve an Equation

When the variable in an equation is multiplied by a fraction, multiply both sides by the reciprocal of the fraction to solve. Multiplying by the reciprocal is the same as dividing.

EXAMPLE 3

Solve.

$$\frac{2}{3}p = -6$$

SOLUTION

$$\frac{2}{3}p = -6$$

$$\frac{2}{3} \cdot \frac{3}{2} \cdot p = -6 \cdot \frac{3}{2} \qquad \text{Multiply both sides of the equation by } \frac{3}{2}.$$

$$1 \cdot p = -9 \qquad \text{Simplify. The product of reciprocals is 1.}$$

$$p = -9 \qquad \text{Identity Property of Multiplication} \quad \blacksquare$$

▶ **Remember** $-6 \cdot \dfrac{3}{2} = -\dfrac{6}{1} \cdot \dfrac{3}{2}$

$$= -\frac{\overset{3}{\cancel{6}}}{1} \cdot \frac{3}{\underset{1}{\cancel{2}}}$$

$$= -\frac{9}{1}$$

$$= -9$$

Application: Science

EXAMPLE 4

Scientists estimate the fish population in a lake every year. In 2008, the estimate was 22,500. The estimate for 2008 was 3 times the estimate for 2005. What was the estimate for 2005?

SOLUTION

Use the words to write an equation. The unknown quantity is the estimate for 2005.

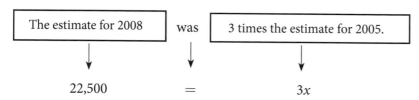

The estimate for 2008	was	3 times the estimate for 2005.
↓	↓	↓
22,500	=	$3x$

Solve the equation.

$$22{,}500 = 3x$$

$$\frac{22{,}500}{3} = \frac{3x}{3} \qquad \text{Divide both sides of the equation by 3.}$$

$$7500 = x \qquad \text{Simplify both sides of the equation.} \ ■$$

▶ **Think About It** When modeling a problem, the words *is* and *was* can often be translated to equals signs.

Equations with Mixed Operations

To solve equations with mixed operations, you need to understand variable terms and indicated operations.

In the equation $5 + 2x = 21$, the variable term is $2x$ and the indicated operations are as follows: The variable is multiplied by 2 and then 5 is added.

In the equation $\frac{t}{3} - 2 = 1$, the variable term is $\frac{t}{3}$ and the indicated operations are as follows: The variable is divided by 3 and then 2 is subtracted.

Solving Simple Equations

To solve an equation, isolate the variable on one side.

In $5 + 2x = 21$, subtract 5 from both sides to isolate the variable term. The result is $2x = 16$. Similarly, in $\frac{t}{3} - 2 = 1$, add 2 to both sides. The result is then $\frac{t}{3} = 3$. If an equation has only one variable term and at most one numerical term on each side, use the method described to isolate the variable. The idea is to peel back the layers one at a time.

How to Solve Simple Equations in One Variable

Undo indicated operations in reverse order.

EXAMPLE 1

Solve and check.

$$3x - 18 = 39$$

SOLUTION

Think: The variable is multiplied by 3, and then 18 is subtracted. To isolate the variable, add 18 and then divide by 3.

$$3x - 18 = 39$$

$$3x - 18 + \mathbf{18} = 39 + \mathbf{18}$$ Add 18 to both sides to undo the subtraction.

$$3x = 57$$

$$\frac{3x}{\mathbf{3}} = \frac{57}{\mathbf{3}}$$ Divide both sides by 3 to undo the multiplication.

$$x = 19$$

> ▶ **Think About It** You can show your addition step in this format:
>
> $$\begin{array}{rcl} 3x - 18 &=& 39 \\ +18 && +18 \\ \hline 3x &=& 57 \end{array}$$

CHECK

$$3x - 18 = 39$$ Start with the original equation.

$$3 \cdot \mathbf{19} - 18 \overset{?}{=} 39$$ Substitute 19 for x.

$$57 - 18 \overset{?}{=} 39$$ Multiply.

$$39 = 39 \checkmark \;\blacksquare$$

> ▶ **Remember** The solution in Example 1 is 19, not 39.

> ▶ **Think About It** Check all solutions. Substitute the solution into the original equation and verify that it makes a true statement.

EXAMPLE 2

Solve.

A $10 + \frac{a}{2} = 2$

SOLUTION

Think: The variable is divided by 2, and then 10 is added. To isolate the variable, subtract 10 and then multiply by 2.

$$10 + \frac{a}{2} = 2$$

$$10 - \mathbf{10} + \frac{a}{2} = 2 - \mathbf{10} \qquad \text{Subtract 10 from both sides to undo the addition.}$$

$$\frac{a}{2} = -8$$

$$\mathbf{2} \cdot \frac{a}{2} = \mathbf{2} \cdot (-8) \qquad \text{Multiply both sides by 2 to undo the division.}$$

$$a = -16$$

▶ **Think About It** In Example 2A, you could start by multiplying by 2, and then you would subtract 20 from each side.

B $-6 = \frac{2}{3}c + 1$

SOLUTION

Think: The variable is multiplied by $\frac{2}{3}$, and then 1 is added. To isolate the variable, subtract 1 and then multiply by $\frac{3}{2}$, which is the reciprocal of $\frac{2}{3}$.

$$-6 = \frac{2}{3}c + 1$$

$$-6 - \mathbf{1} = \frac{2}{3}c + 1 - \mathbf{1} \qquad \text{Subtract 1 from both sides to undo the addition.}$$

$$-7 = \frac{2}{3}c$$

$$\mathbf{\frac{3}{2}} \cdot (-7) = \mathbf{\frac{3}{2}} \cdot \frac{2}{3}c \qquad \text{Multiply both sides by } \frac{3}{2} \text{ to undo the multiplication.}$$

$$-\frac{21}{2} = 1 \cdot c$$

$$-\frac{21}{2} = c$$

C $\dfrac{x+1}{3} = -5$

SOLUTION

Think: First 1 is added to the variable, and then the result is divided by 3. To isolate the variable, multiply by 3 and then subtract 1.

$$\frac{x+1}{3} = -5$$

$$3 \cdot \frac{x+1}{3} = 3 \cdot (-5) \qquad \text{Multiply both sides by 3 to undo the division.}$$

$$x + 1 = -15$$

$$x + 1 - 1 = -15 - 1 \qquad \text{Subtract 1 from both sides to undo the addition.}$$

$$x = -16 \; \blacksquare$$

Combining Like Terms to Solve Equations

To solve some equations, it helps to simplify expressions by combining like terms. You don't absolutely have to simplify first, but a simpler equation reduces your risk of making mistakes.

EXAMPLE 3

Solve.

$$5x + 5 - 8x - 4 = -29$$

SOLUTION

$$5x + 5 - 8x - 4 = -29$$

$$-3x + 1 = -29 \qquad \text{Combine like terms on the left side.}$$

$$-3x + 1 - 1 = -29 - 1 \qquad \text{Subtract 1 from both sides to undo the addition.}$$

$$-3x = -30$$

$$\frac{-3x}{-3} = \frac{-30}{-3} \qquad \text{Divide both sides by } -3 \text{ to undo the multiplication.}$$

$$x = 10 \ \blacksquare$$

Solving Equations That Have the Variable on Both Sides

If the variable appears on both sides of the equation, add or subtract a variable term so that the variable appears on only one side.

EXAMPLE 4

Solve.

$$3x + 1 = 5x - 7$$

SOLUTION

$$3x + 1 = 5x - 7$$

$$3x - 3x + 1 = 5x - 3x - 7 \qquad \text{Subtract } 3x \text{ from both sides so that the variable appears on only one side.}$$

$$1 = 2x - 7$$

$$1 + 7 = 2x - 7 + 7 \qquad \text{Add 7 to both sides to undo the subtraction.}$$

$$8 = 2x$$

$$\frac{8}{2} = \frac{2x}{2} \qquad \text{Divide both sides by 2 to undo the multiplication.}$$

$$4 = x \ \blacksquare$$

Solving Equations: The Distributive Property

You have learned that the distributive property has several different uses.

Removing parentheses	Combining like terms
$7(a + b) = 7a + 7b$	$4n + 5n = (4 + 5)n = 9n$

The distributive property can be very helpful in solving equations that include parentheses.

EXAMPLE 5

Solve.

A $4(x - 5) = 8$

SOLUTION

$$4(x - 5) = 8$$

$$4x - 20 = 8 \qquad \text{Apply the distributive property to remove parentheses.}$$

$$4x - 20 + 20 = 8 + 20 \qquad \text{Add 20 to both sides to undo the subtraction.}$$

$$4x = 28$$

$$\frac{4x}{4} = \frac{28}{4} \qquad \text{Divide both sides by 4 to undo the multiplication.}$$

$$x = 7$$

B $\frac{1}{3}(1 + 6x) = -1 + 3x$

SOLUTION

$$\frac{1}{3}(1 + 6x) = -1 + 3x$$

$$\frac{1}{3} + 2x = -1 + 3x \qquad \text{Apply the distributive property to remove parentheses.}$$

$$\frac{1}{3} + 2x - 2x = -1 + 3x - 2x \qquad \text{Subtract } 2x \text{ from both sides to undo the addition.}$$

$$\frac{1}{3} = -1 + x$$

$$\frac{1}{3} + 1 = -1 + 1 + x \qquad \text{Add 1 to both sides to undo the subtraction.}$$

$$1\frac{1}{3} = x \ \blacksquare$$

▶ **Q&A**

Q How could you eliminate the fraction $\frac{1}{3}$ in the first step of Example 5B?

You would still use the distributive property by distributing 3 over the sum at the right side of equation.

A Multiply both sides of the equation by 3.

Application: Using the Distributive Property

EXAMPLE 6

A rectangular park is 30 yd long and 20 yd wide. The city plans to extend the length of the park so that it has a total area of 760 yd². How much must the length of the park be extended?

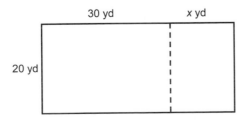

SOLUTION

Let x represent the amount the length must be extended. The enlarged park will have a width of 20 yd and a length of $30 + x$ yards. Since the area of a rectangle is the width times the length, the equation $20(30 + x) = 760$ represents the situation.

$$20(30 + x) = 760$$

$$\mathbf{600 + 20x} = 760 \qquad \text{Apply the distributive property to remove parentheses.}$$

$$600 - \mathbf{600} + 20x = 760 - \mathbf{600} \qquad \text{Subtract 600 from both sides to undo the addition.}$$

$$20x = 160$$

$$\frac{20x}{\mathbf{20}} = \frac{160}{\mathbf{20}} \qquad \text{Divide both sides by 20 to undo the multiplication.}$$

$$x = 8$$

The length of the park must be extended 8 yd. ∎

Application: Number Problem

EXAMPLE 7

Three more than twice a number is 31. What is the number?

SOLUTION

Let n represent the number.

Three more than twice the number is 31.

$$3 \qquad + \qquad 2n \qquad = \quad 31 \qquad \text{Write the equation.}$$

$$2n \qquad = \quad 28 \qquad \text{Subtract 3 from both sides.}$$

$$n \qquad = \quad 14 \qquad \text{Divide by 2.}$$

The number is 14. ∎

Application: Simple Interest

EXAMPLE 8

Andy deposited some money to open a bank account that paid 8% simple interest. He made no other deposits or withdrawals. At the end of 1 year, the balance was $270. How much did Andy deposit?

SOLUTION

Let x represent the amount Andy deposited.

amount deposited	plus	8% simple interest	was	$270	
x	$+$	$0.08x$	$=$	270	Write the equation.
$1.00x$	$+$	$0.08x$	$=$	270	Write x as $1.00x$.
		$1.08x$	$=$	270	Combine like terms.
		$\dfrac{1.08x}{1.08}$	$=$	$\dfrac{270.00}{1.08}$	Solve the equation.
		x	$=$	250	

Andy deposited $250. ■

Inequalities

Working with inequalities is similar to working with equations.

Identifying Solutions of Inequalities

Definitions

An **inequality** is a mathematical sentence that compares numbers or expressions using one of the symbols $<$, $>$, $\leq$, or $\geq$.

A **solution** of a one-variable inequality is a value for the variable that makes the inequality true.

The set of all solutions of an inequality is the **solution set** of the inequality.

EXAMPLE 1

Identify the solution set of the inequality $x > -3$, using the replacement set $\{-5, -3.5, -3, -2, 0, 1\}$.

SOLUTION
Determine which of the numbers are to the right of -3 on a number line.

Using the replacement set, only the numbers -2, 0, and 1 are to the right of -3. The solution set is $\{-2, 0, 1\}$. ∎

Graphing Simple Inequalities

Most inequalities that have a solution have an infinite number of solutions.

The **graph of a one-variable inequality** is the set of points on a number line that represents all the solutions of the inequality.

When graphing a one-variable inequality, draw an open dot if the endpoint is not a solution and draw a solid dot if the endpoint is a solution. Draw a shaded arrow on one side of the endpoint to show the solutions. The table shows some simple one-variable inequalities and their graphs.

Inequality	Words	Graph
$x < 2$	x is less than 2.	
$n > -1$	n is greater than -1.	
$s \leq 0$	s is less than or equal to 0.	
$a \geq 4.35$	a is greater than or equal to 4.35.	

Solving and Graphing Inequalities

Equivalent inequalities are inequalities that have the same solution set. The properties of order tell you how to obtain equivalent inequalities by adding, subtracting, multiplying, and dividing.

Properties of Order

Property	Example
Addition and Subtraction Properties of Order Adding or subtracting the same number on both sides of an inequality produces an equivalent inequality.	
If $a > b$, then $a + c > b + c$. If $a < b$, then $a + c < b + c$. If $a \geq b$, then $a + c \geq b + c$. If $a \leq b$, then $a + c \leq b + c$. If $a > b$, then $a - c > b - c$. If $a < b$, then $a - c < b - c$. If $a \geq b$, then $a - c \geq b - c$. If $a \leq b$, then $a - c \leq b - c$.	If $5 > 2$, then $5 + 6 > 2 + 6$. If $x > 3$, then $x + 4 > 3 + 4$. If $u + 5 \leq 11$, then $u + 5 - 5 \leq 11 - 5$.
Multiplication and Division Properties of Order (Positive Multiplier/Divisor) Multiplying or dividing both sides of an inequality by a positive number produces an equivalent inequality.	
For any $c > 0$, If $a > b$, then $a \cdot c > b \cdot c$. If $a < b$, then $a \cdot c < b \cdot c$. If $a \geq b$, then $a \cdot c \geq b \cdot c$. If $a \leq b$, then $a \cdot c \leq b \cdot c$. If $a > b$, then $\dfrac{a}{c} > \dfrac{b}{c}$. If $a < b$, then $\dfrac{a}{c} < \dfrac{b}{c}$. If $a \geq b$, then $\dfrac{a}{c} \geq \dfrac{b}{c}$. If $a \leq b$, then $\dfrac{a}{c} \leq \dfrac{b}{c}$.	If $2 < 3$, then $4 \cdot 2 < 4 \cdot 3$. If $2x \geq 6$, then $\dfrac{2x}{2} \geq \dfrac{6}{2}$.

Continued

Properties of Order (Continued)

Property

Example

Multiplication and Division Properties of Order (Negative Multiplier/Divisor)
Multiplying or dividing both sides of an inequality by a negative number and reversing the direction of the inequality symbol produces an equivalent inequality.

For any $c < 0$,
If $a > b$, then $a \bullet c < b \bullet c$.
If $a < b$, then $a \bullet c > b \bullet c$.
If $a \geq b$, then $a \bullet c \leq b \bullet c$.
If $a \leq b$, then $a \bullet c \geq b \bullet c$.

If $a > b$, then $\dfrac{a}{c} < \dfrac{b}{c}$.

If $a < b$, then $\dfrac{a}{c} > \dfrac{b}{c}$.

If $a \geq b$, then $\dfrac{a}{c} \leq \dfrac{b}{c}$.

If $a \leq b$, then $\dfrac{a}{c} \geq \dfrac{b}{c}$.

If $\dfrac{a}{-3} < 5$,

then $-3\left(\dfrac{a}{-3}\right) > -3 \bullet 5.$

If $12 > 8$, then $\dfrac{12}{-4} < \dfrac{8}{-4}.$

Multiply both sides by -2 and see what happens.

$$5 > 2$$
$$5 \bullet (-2) \overset{?}{>} 2 \bullet (-2)$$
$$-10 < -4$$

▶ **Think About It** Note that the inequality symbol changes when you multiply through by a negative number.

The method of solving an inequality is similar to the method of solving an equation. Use inverse operations along with the properties of order to obtain simpler inequalities that are equivalent. When you have the simplest equivalent inequality, you have the statement that best describes the solution set. When you have that statement, graph it.

EXAMPLE 2

Solve and graph the inequality.

A $5x - 10 < 60$

SOLUTION

$$5x - 10 < 60$$

$$5x - 10 + \mathbf{10} < 60 + \mathbf{10} \qquad \text{Add 10 to both sides.}$$

$$5x < 70$$

$$\frac{5x}{5} < \frac{70}{5} \qquad \text{Divide both sides by 5.}$$

$$x < 14$$

▶ **Think About It** The graph represents all the inequalities in Example 2A because they are all equivalent. The simplest inequality, $x < 14$, is the statement that best describes the graph or the solution set.

B $\frac{-t}{3} \geq 2$

SOLUTION

$$\frac{-t}{3} \geq 2$$

$$-\mathbf{3} \cdot \left(\frac{-t}{3}\right) \leq -\mathbf{3} \cdot 2 \qquad \text{Multiply both sides by } -3. \text{ Reverse the inequality symbol.}$$

$$t \leq -6$$

▶ **Remember** When graphing, draw an open dot for the symbols $<$ and $>$. Draw a solid dot for the symbols $\leq$ and $\geq$.

C $2(a + 2) - a > 0$

SOLUTION

$2(a + 2) - a > 0$

$2a + 4 - a > 0$ Apply the distributive property.

$a + 4 > 0$ Combine like terms.

$a + 4 - \mathbf{4} > 0 - \mathbf{4}$ Subtract 4 from both sides.

$a > -4$

D $3 > -\dfrac{5x + 1}{2}$

SOLUTION

$3 > -\dfrac{5x + 1}{2}$

$3 > -\dfrac{1}{2}(5x + 1)$ Write $-\dfrac{5x + 1}{2}$ as $-\dfrac{1}{2}(5x + 1)$.

$-\mathbf{2} \cdot 3 < -\mathbf{2} \cdot \left(-\dfrac{1}{2}\right)(5x + 1)$ Multiply both sides by -2. Reverse the inequality symbol.

$-6 < 5x + 1$

$-6 - \mathbf{1} < 5x + 1 - \mathbf{1}$ Subtract 1 from both sides.

$-7 < 5x$

$\dfrac{-7}{5} < \dfrac{5x}{5}$ Divide both sides by 5.

$-\dfrac{7}{5} < x$

▶ **Remember** In general, $a < b$ is equivalent to $b > a$. In Example 2D, $-\dfrac{7}{5} < x$ is equivalent to $x > -\dfrac{7}{5}$.

Application: Comparing Membership Fees

EXAMPLE 3

Eli is deciding whether to join Gym A or Gym B. Gym A costs $50 to join and $31.50/month. Gym B costs $170 to join and $24/month. For what length of time will it cost less to belong to Gym A?

SOLUTION

Let x represent the number of months Eli has a gym membership.

cost of Gym A $<$ cost of Gym B

$50 + 31.50x < 170 + 24x$ — Write an inequality to represent the situation.

$50 + 31.50x - \mathbf{24x} < 170 + 24x - \mathbf{24x}$ — Subtract $24x$ from both sides so that the variable appears on only one side.

$50 + 7.50x < 170$

$50 - \mathbf{50} + 7.50x < 170 - \mathbf{50}$ — Subtract 50 from both sides.

$7.50x < 120$

$\dfrac{7.50x}{7.50} < \dfrac{120}{7.50}$ — Divide both sides by 7.50.

$x < 16$

It will cost less to belong to Gym A for any number of months less than 16 months. ▪

Applications of Inequalities

Many real-world situations involve a quantity that has a minimum or maximum possible value. An inequality can represent a quantity that is at least or no more than some value.

Representing Inequalities

Translate a problem statement into an inequality by translating words and phrases into variables, operators $(+, -, \times, \div)$, and inequality symbols $(<, \leq, >, \geq)$, just as you would for any problem involving an equation.

EXAMPLE 1

Adele is swimming laps at swim practice. To prevent injury, Adele's coach tells her to swim no more than 2400 m that day. Each lap is 50 m. Adele has swum 600 m so far.

> ▶ **Remember** A lap in a swimming pool is down the length of the pool and back. If a pool is 25 m long, one lap is
>
> $$2 \times 25 \text{ m} = 50 \text{ m}.$$

A Write an inequality that expresses how many more laps Adele can swim at practice. Explain your reasoning.

SOLUTION
Let n represent the number of laps Adele can swim without exceeding her coach's recommendation. This distance, in meters, is the product of the number of laps and the length of 1 lap, equal to $50n$.

The sum of the distance Adele has already swum, 600 m, and the remaining distance she can swim, 50n meters, can be no more than 2400 m. Written as an inequality, this is

$$600 + 50n \leq 2400.$$

> **Think About It** Certain phrases suggest representing a real-world situation as an inequality with a $\leq$ sign:
>
> - at most
>
> - maximum
>
> - no more than

B Solve the inequality in Example 1A.

SOLUTION

$$600 + 50n \leq 2400$$
$$600 - \mathbf{600} + 50n \leq 2400 - \mathbf{600}$$
$$50n \leq 1800$$
$$\frac{50n}{\mathbf{50}} \leq \frac{1800}{\mathbf{50}}$$
$$n \leq 36$$

Adele can swim no more than 36 more laps. ■

EXAMPLE 2

Ibrahim wants to buy a new pair of basketball shoes. He has $55 right now. New basketball shoes cost $133 or more. Ibrahim earns $12/h tutoring.

A Write an inequality that expresses the minimum number of hours Ibrahim needs to work to earn enough money to buy new basketball shoes. Explain your reasoning.

SOLUTION
Let h represent the number of hours Ibrahim must work to earn enough additional money. This amount, in dollars, is the product of his hourly wage and the number of hours he works at this rate, or $12h$.

The sum of the amount of money Ibrahim already has, $55, and the amount of money he still needs, $12h$ dollars, must be at least $133. Written as an inequality, this is

$$55 + 12h \geq 133.$$

B Solve the inequality in Example 2A.

SOLUTION

$$55 + 12h \geq 133$$
$$55 - \mathbf{55} + 12h \geq 133 - \mathbf{55}$$
$$12h \geq 78$$
$$\frac{12h}{\mathbf{12}} \geq \frac{78}{\mathbf{12}}$$
$$h \geq 6\frac{1}{2} \text{ or } h \geq 6.5$$

Ibrahim needs to work at least another 6.5 h to have enough money for new basketball shoes. ▪

Plane Figures

Topic List

You can find geometric shapes, including triangles and parallel lines, in art. Artists need to understand angles and shapes to create beautiful objects and to solve practical problems.

Similarity and Scale

Similar figures are figures that have the exact same shape but not necessarily the same size.

▶ **Remember** Congruent angles are angles having equal measures.

Figures are similar if corresponding angles are congruent and corresponding sides are proportional.

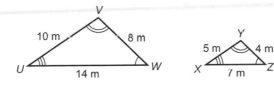

$\triangle UVW$ is similar to $\triangle XYZ$ so

$$\angle U \cong \angle X, \quad \angle V \cong \angle Y, \quad \angle W \cong \angle Z$$

$$\frac{UV}{XY} = \frac{VW}{YZ}; \frac{UV}{XY} = \frac{WU}{ZX}; \frac{VW}{YZ} = \frac{WU}{ZX}$$

▶ **Think About It** UV means the length of $\overline{UV}$.

Cross multiply to see if the fractions are equal.

$$\frac{10}{5} \overset{?}{=} \frac{8}{4}$$
$$10 \cdot 4 \overset{?}{=} 5 \cdot 8$$
$$40 = 40 \checkmark$$

$$\frac{10}{5} \overset{?}{=} \frac{14}{7}$$
$$10 \cdot 7 \overset{?}{=} 5 \cdot 14$$
$$70 = 70 \checkmark$$

$$\frac{8}{4} \overset{?}{=} \frac{14}{7}$$
$$8 \cdot 7 \overset{?}{=} 4 \cdot 14$$
$$56 = 56 \checkmark$$

Determining Whether Two Figures Are Similar

EXAMPLE 1

Determine whether rectangles *ABCD* and *EFGH* are similar.

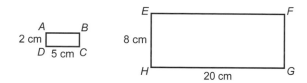

SOLUTION

Step 1 Check corresponding angles.

Because both figures are rectangles, all angles measure 90°.
Thus, $\angle A \cong \angle E$; $\angle B \cong \angle F$; $\angle C \cong \angle G$; $\angle D \cong \angle H$.

Therefore, corresponding angles are congruent.

Step 2 Check corresponding sides.

If corresponding sides are proportional, then $\dfrac{AD}{EH} = \dfrac{AB}{EF}$.

$\dfrac{2}{8} \overset{?}{=} \dfrac{5}{20}$ Write the measures of the side lengths as a proportion and check to see if the proportion is true.

$2 \cdot 20 \overset{?}{=} 8 \cdot 5$ Cross multiply to see if the fractions are equal.

$40 = 40 \checkmark$

Because corresponding angles are congruent and corresponding sides are proportional, the rectangles are similar. ∎

Using Similarity to Find Missing Side Lengths

You can use the properties of similar figures to find a missing side.

EXAMPLE 2

$\triangle GHI$ and $\triangle JKL$ are similar. What is the length of $\overline{JK}$?

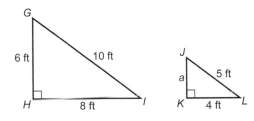

> **Remember** In the proportion $\dfrac{a}{b} = \dfrac{c}{d}$, a and d are the extremes, and b and c are the means. The product of the means equals the product of the extremes.

SOLUTION

$\overline{GH}$ corresponds to $\overline{JK}$. $\overline{HI}$ corresponds to KL. Set up the corresponding sides as a proportion. Then solve for a.

$\dfrac{6}{a} = \dfrac{8}{4}$ Write a proportion.

$6 \cdot 4 = 8a$ Cross multiply.

$\dfrac{24}{8} = \dfrac{8a}{8}$ Divide both sides by 8.

$3 = a$ Simplify.

The length of $\overline{JK}$ is 3 ft. ■

Determining Scale

A **scale factor** is a ratio of one measure to another. You can find a scale factor of a figure by using the ratio of corresponding parts.

original   new size

4 cm   6 cm

The new size is an enlargement and therefore is similar to the original figure. To find the scale factor, write a ratio comparing corresponding sides.

$$\frac{\text{new size}}{\text{original size}} = \frac{6 \text{ cm}}{4 \text{ cm}} = \frac{3}{2}$$

The scale factor for the arrows is 3 : 2 or 1.5.

EXAMPLE 3

The regular pentagons shown are similar. What is the scale factor?

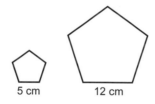

5 cm   12 cm

▶ **Think About It** All regular pentagons are similar to each other.

SOLUTION

These figures show an enlargement, so the scale factor is greater than 1.

The scale factor is $\frac{12}{5}$. ■

Using a Scale Factor

A scale factor greater than 1 indicates an enlargement. A scale factor less than 1 indicates a reduction. A scale factor equal to 1 means there is no change in size.

EXAMPLE 4

An equilateral triangle with a side length of 8 cm is multiplied by the scale factor. State whether the new triangle is an enlargement or a reduction. Then find the side length of the new size.

A $\frac{3}{4}$

SOLUTION

This triangle is a reduction because the scale factor is less than 1. Multiplying by the scale factor, you have $\frac{3}{4} \cdot 8 = 6$. The new side measure is 6 cm.

B 2.2

SOLUTION

This triangle is an enlargement because the scale factor is greater than 1. Multiplying by the scale factor, you have $2.2 \cdot 8 = 17.6$. The new side measure is 17.6 cm. ■

Application: Photography

EXAMPLE 5

A rectangular picture is 2.5 in. wide and 4 in. long. If the picture is enlarged so that it is 10 in. long, what is the new width?

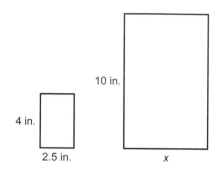

SOLUTION

Because the figures show an enlargement, the pictures will be similar.

$\dfrac{2.5}{x} = \dfrac{4}{10}$ Set up a proportion using corresponding sides.

$2.5 \cdot 10 = 4x$ Cross multiply.

$\dfrac{25}{4} = \dfrac{4x}{4}$ Divide both sides by 4.

$6.25 = x$ Simplify.

The width of the enlarged picture is 6.25 in. ▪

Triangles

Many figures can be formed when parts of lines, rather than lines, are used.

Definition

A **line segment** is part of a line. It includes any two points on the line and all the points between those points.

A line segment is named by its endpoints. The points can be written in any order: segment ST, segment TS, $\overline{ST}$, or $\overline{TS}$.

▶ **Think About It** A line segment is often more simply called a segment.

Definition

A **triangle** is a figure made up of three segments joined at their endpoints. Each endpoint is a vertex.

To name a triangle, use all three vertices. They can be listed in any order. Two possible names for this triangle are $\triangle FGH$ or $\triangle GHF$.

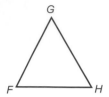

▶ **Think About It** The plural of *vertex* is *vertices*.

Classifying Triangles by Angle Measures

Every triangle can be classified according to its angle measures.

Definitions
An **acute triangle** is a triangle with three acute angles.
A **right triangle** is a triangle with a right angle.
An **obtuse triangle** is a triangle with an obtuse angle.

EXAMPLE 1

Classify the triangle as acute, right, or obtuse.

A

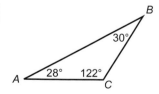

SOLUTION
Because $m\angle C > 90°$, $\angle C$ is an obtuse angle, so the triangle is an obtuse triangle.

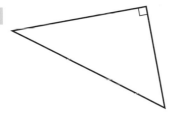

SOLUTION

Because one of the angles is a right angle, the triangle is a right triangle. ■

Using the Triangle Angle Sum Property

▶ **Think About It** It is not possible for a triangle to have more than one right angle or more than one obtuse angle.

Triangle Angle Sum Property

The sum of the measures of the angles of any triangle is 180°.

$$m\angle 1 + m\angle 2 + m\angle 3 = 180°$$

EXAMPLE 2

Find the value of x in the triangle.

A

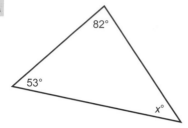

SOLUTION

Find the sum of the measures of the two known angles.

$$82° + 53° = 135°$$

Subtract this sum from 180°.

$$180° - 135° = 45°$$
$$x = 45$$

▶ **Think About It** In Example 2A, you can also solve the equation $x + 82 + 53 = 180$.

B

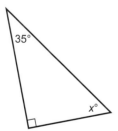

SOLUTION

Because the triangle is a right triangle, the sum of the measures of the two acute angles must be 90°.

$$x + 35 = 90$$
$$x + 35 - 35 = 90 - 35$$
$$x = 55 \ \blacksquare$$

Application: Home Improvement

EXAMPLE 3

A homeowner leans a ladder against her house so that the bottom of the ladder makes a 62° angle with the ground. What angle does the top of the ladder make with the building?

SOLUTION
Draw a model. Assume that the ground is perpendicular to the building. The ladder, ground, and building form a right triangle.

$$x + 62 = 90$$
$$x = 90 - 62$$
$$x = 28$$

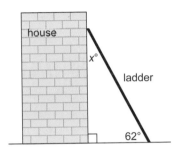

> **Think About It** Two lines, or segments, that form right angles are perpendicular to each other.

CHECK
$$28 + 62 + 90 = 180 \checkmark$$

The top of the ladder makes a 28° angle with the building. ▪

Constructing Geometric Shapes

You can use a ruler and a protractor to construct the sides and the angles that define a geometric shape.

Constructing Angles

How to Construct Angles

To construct an angle with a given measure,

Step 1 Use a ruler to draw a line segment.

Step 2 Place the protractor along the drawn line segment so it lies along the 0° base of the protractor and one endpoint is at the protractor's vertex.

Step 3 Make a mark at the degree measure of the angle.

Step 4 Draw the second segment from the mark to the endpoint of the first line segment that lies at the protractor's vertex.

Step 5 If the line segments forming the angle are to be a given length, place the ruler at the vertex of the angle and then mark each segment at the desired length.

EXAMPLE 1

Construct an angle with the given measure.

A 90° (right angle)

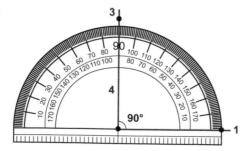

SOLUTION

Step 1 Place the ruler on the paper and draw a horizontal line segment forming one side of the angle.

Step 2 Place the protractor on the paper so that the crossbar lines up with the left endpoint of the line segment drawn.

Step 3 Make a mark at the desired degree measure, 90°.

Step 4 Remove the protractor and draw a line segment connecting the mark to the left endpoint of the first line segment.

B 45°, with side lengths of 3 cm

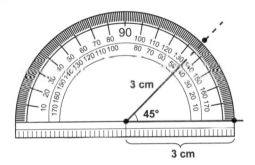

SOLUTION

Step 1 Place the ruler on the paper and draw a horizontal line segment 3 cm long.

Step 2 Place the protractor on the paper so that the crossbar lines up with the left endpoint of the line segment drawn.

Step 3 Make a mark at the desired degree measure, 45°.

Step 4 Remove the protractor and draw a line segment connecting the mark to the left endpoint of the first line segment.

Step 5 Mark a length of 3 cm on the second segment. ■

Constructing Triangles

You can construct a triangle if you know the measures of all three angles or are given enough information to find the measures of all three angles. Use a ruler to draw the line segments forming the angle, and use a protractor to construct angles with the given measures.

EXAMPLE 2

Construct an equilateral triangle with side lengths of 2 cm.

SOLUTION

Step 1 Place the ruler on the paper and draw a horizontal line segment 2 cm long.

Step 2 Place the protractor on the paper so that the crossbar lines up with the left endpoint of the line segment drawn.

Step 3 Make a mark at the 60° measure.

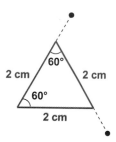

Step 4 Remove the protractor and draw a line segment connecting the mark to the left endpoint of the first line segment. Adjust the length of the line segment so that it is 2 cm long.

Step 5 Repeat Step 2 for the apex (top) angle.

Step 6 Repeat Step 3, connecting the second line segment to the right endpoint of the first line segment, forming an equilateral triangle. ■

You can measure the angles of the triangle with the protractor to verify that each angle measures 60°.

EXAMPLE 3

Construct an isosceles triangle with two sides equal to 3 cm and an included angle of 40°.

SOLUTION

Step 1 Place the ruler on the paper and draw a horizontal line segment 3 cm long.

Step 2 Use the protractor to construct a 40° angle.

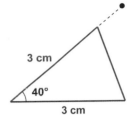

Step 3 Remove the protractor and draw a line segment connecting the mark to the left endpoint of the first line segment. Adjust the length of the line segment so that it is 3 cm long.

Step 4 Connect the second line segment to the right endpoint of the first line segment, forming an isosceles triangle. ■

Constructing Right Triangles

You can construct a right triangle given only its side lengths. First draw the two shorter sides of the triangle with the right angle between them. Then draw the hypotenuse by connecting the endpoints of the other two sides, thus completing the triangle.

▶ **Think About It** The two shorter sides that form the right angle in a right triangle are also known as the **legs** of the right triangle.

▶ **Remember** The hypotenuse is the longest side in a right triangle. Also, it is always opposite the right angle.

EXAMPLE 4

Construct a right triangle with side lengths equal to 3, 4, and 5 cm. The base of the triangle is the 3 cm side.

SOLUTION

Step 1 Place the ruler on the paper and draw a horizontal line segment 3 cm long.

Step 2 Use the protractor to construct a 90° (right) angle.

Step 3 Draw a line segment connecting the mark to the left endpoint of the first line segment. Adjust the length of the line segment so that it is 4 cm long.

Step 4 Connect the top endpoint of the second line segment to the right endpoint of the first line segment, forming a hypotenuse 5 cm long. ▪

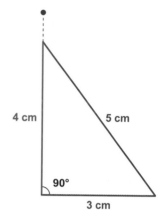

Constructing Quadrilaterals

You can use a ruler and a protractor to construct a rectangle given only its length and width. You can also use a ruler and a protractor to construct a right trapezoid given its height and the lengths of both bases.

EXAMPLE 5

Construct a rectangle with a length of 2.5 cm and a width of 3 cm.

▶ **Remember** The opposite sides of a rectangle are parallel and equal in length. All interior angles of a rectangle are right angles, or 90°.

SOLUTION

Step 1 Place the ruler on the paper and draw a horizontal line segment 2.5 cm long.

Step 2 Use the protractor to mark a 90° (right) angle at the left endpoint of the line segment.

Step 3 Draw a second line segment connecting the 90° mark to the left endpoint of the first line segment. Use the ruler to adjust the length of the second line segment so that it is 3 cm long.

Step 4 Use the protractor to mark another 90° (right) angle at the right endpoint of the first line segment.

Step 5 Draw a third line segment connecting the 90° mark to the right endpoint of the first line segment. Use the ruler to adjust the length of the third line segment so that it is 3 cm long.

Step 6 Connect the top endpoint of the second line segment to the top endpoint of the third line segment, forming a side that is 2.5 cm long. ■

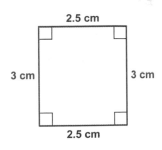

EXAMPLE 6

Construct a right trapezoid with a height of in $1\frac{1}{2}$ in., one base that is $2\frac{3}{4}$ in., and the other base that is 2 in.

> ▶ **Remember** A trapezoid has one pair of parallel lines. A right trapezoid has two interior right angles.

SOLUTION

Step 1 Place the ruler on the paper and draw a horizontal line segment $2\frac{3}{4}$ in. long. This is one base of the trapezoid.

Step 2 Use the protractor to mark a 90° (right) angle at the left endpoint of the line segment.

Step 3 Draw a second line segment connecting the mark to the left endpoint of the first line segment. Use the ruler to adjust the length of the second line segment so that it is $1\frac{1}{2}$ in. long. This is the height of the trapezoid.

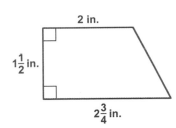

Step 4 Use the protractor to mark a 90° (right) angle at the top endpoint of the second line segment.

Step 5 Draw a third line segment connecting the mark to the top endpoint of the second line segment. Adjust the length of the third line segment so that it is 2 in. long. This is the other base of the trapezoid.

Step 6 Connect the right endpoint of the third line segment to the right endpoint of the first line segment, forming a fourth line segment to complete the right trapezoid. ■

How Many Triangles?

You can determine how many triangles fit a given description by applying triangle math facts.

Finding How Many Triangles Are Possible, Given Angle Measures

Sum of the Interior Angle Measures of a Triangle

The sum of the measures of a triangle's three interior angles is always equal to 180°.

To find how many triangles fit a given description, first use triangle math facts to determine whether it is possible to construct even one triangle fitting that description. If at least one triangle is possible, use any side length information you have to work through different possibilities for triangle shapes.

▶ **Q&A**

Q How many equilateral triangles are possible?

A an infinite number; Although all three angles measure 60°, there is an infinite number of possible side lengths.

EXAMPLE 1

How many triangles are possible with the given characteristics: zero, one, or more than one? Explain your reasoning.

A angles whose measures are 50°, 50°, and 80°

SOLUTION

The sum of the measures of the three angles is $50° + 50° + 80° = 180°$. The triangle is an isosceles triangle, but you don't know any of the side lengths. Therefore, you can construct infinitely many similar triangles, all with angle measures of 50°, 50°, and 80°. More than one triangle is possible.

B two angles whose measures are 30° and 50°, and one side 4 cm in length

> ▶ **Think About It** Knowing the measure of two of a triangle's interior angles is enough to determine the measure of the third interior angle.

SOLUTION

Because two of the angle measures are 30° and 50°, the measure of the third angle must be $180° - (30° + 50°) = 180° - 80° = 100°$. However, any of the three sides could be 4 cm in length. You can confirm this by setting each of the sides equal to 4 cm and then measuring the lengths of the other two sides.

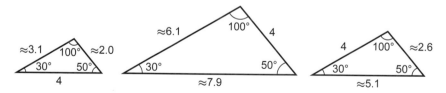

More than one triangle is possible. ■

Finding How Many Triangles Are Possible, Given Only Side Lengths

Triangle Side Lengths

The length of any side of a triangle is always shorter than the sum of the lengths of the other two sides.

To determine how many triangles are possible based on side length, find the sum of the lengths of the two shorter sides and compare that to the length of the longest side. If the longest side is shorter than the two other sides combined, then exactly one triangle is possible. If the longest side is longer than or equal to the sum of the two other sides, then no triangle is possible.

EXAMPLE 2

How many triangles are possible with the given characteristics: zero, one, or more than one? Use a sketch to illustrate your reasoning.

A side lengths of 4, 6, and 12 units

SOLUTION
The sum of the lengths of the two shorter sides is $4 + 6 = 10$ units.

If the longest side were equal to 10 (the sum of the other two sides), then the angle included between these two sides would have to equal 180°, and no triangle could exist.

▶ **Remember** An angle that measures 180° is known as a **straight angle**.

Therefore, to make an angle of less than 180° between the two shorter sides, the longest side must be less than 10.

In this case, the longest side is 12 units (i.e., greater than 10), so no triangle is possible.

B side lengths of 2, 4, and 5 cm

SOLUTION

The sum of the lengths of the two shorter sides is $2 + 4 = 6$ cm. The longest side is 5 cm, which is less than the sum of the two shorter sides, so exactly one triangle exists.

A right triangle with legs 2 and 4 has a hypotenuse that is too short.

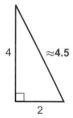

With some trial-and-error, you can find that an angle of 110° is about right.

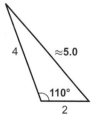

Using a ruler, you can draw a right triangle with legs of 2 and 4 cm. If you measure the hypotenuse, you see that it is shorter than 5 cm. If you increase the angle between the two shorter sides, you see that a measure of about 110° makes a triangle with the given side lengths of 2, 4, and 5 cm. One triangle is possible. ∎

Pairs of Angles

Some angle pairs are special because of their orientation or the sum of their measures.

> ▶ **Think About It** If a point is in the interior of an angle, then it lies on a segment that has one endpoint on one of the angle's rays and the other endpoint on the other ray.

In relation to an angle, a point can be in one of three places. Here, point B is on the angle, point D is in the interior of the angle, and point E is in the exterior of the angle.

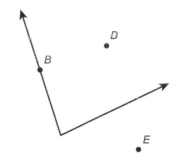

If angles in the same plane share a vertex and a side, but do not share any interior points, they are **adjacent angles**. Angles 1 and 2 are adjacent.

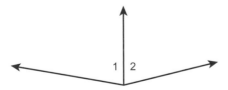

Identifying Linear Pairs and Vertical Angles

Definitions

A **linear pair** is made up of two angles that have a common side and whose other sides point in opposite directions.

Vertical angles are a pair of nonadjacent angles formed by two intersecting lines.

▶ **Think About It** A linear pair is always an adjacent pair of angles.

EXAMPLE 1

Given that $\overleftrightarrow{RQ}$ and $\overleftrightarrow{NT}$ intersect at point E, identify the pair of angles as a linear pair, vertical angles, adjacent angles that are not a linear pair, or none of these.

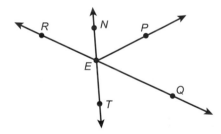

A $\angle REN$ and $\angle TEQ$

SOLUTION
They are nonadjacent angles formed by $\overleftrightarrow{RQ}$ and $\overleftrightarrow{NT}$.
They are vertical angles.

B $\angle RET$ and $\angle NEP$

SOLUTION
They are nonadjacent angles, but they are not formed from two intersecting lines. The answer is none of these.

C ∠*NER* and ∠*RET*

SOLUTION

They are adjacent angles with common side $\overrightarrow{ER}$. The other sides, $\overrightarrow{EN}$ and $\overrightarrow{ET}$, point in opposite directions, forming a line. The angles form a linear pair.

D ∠*NEP* and ∠*PEQ*

SOLUTION

They are adjacent angles with common side $\overrightarrow{EP}$. The other sides, $\overrightarrow{EN}$ and $\overrightarrow{EQ}$, do not form a line. They are adjacent angles that do not form a linear pair. ■

Using Properties of Angle Pairs

Properties of Angle Pairs

The sum of the angle measures in a linear pair is 180°.

Vertical angles have equal measures.

EXAMPLE 2

Find the angle measure.

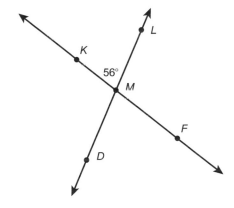

A Find $m\angle KMD$.

> ▶ **Think About It** A lowercase *m* before an angle means "the measure of," so $m\angle KMD$ means the measure of angle *KMD*.

SOLUTION

$\angle KMD$ and $\angle KML$ form a linear pair.

Write and solve an equation.

$$m\angle KMD + m\angle KML = 180°$$

$$x + 56° = 180° \qquad \text{Substitute.}$$

$$x = 180° - 56° \qquad \text{Subtract 56° from both sides.}$$

$$x = 124° \qquad \text{Simplify.}$$

The measure of $\angle KMD$ is 124°.

B Find $m\angle LMF$.

SOLUTION

$\angle LMF$ and $\angle KMD$ are vertical angles, so their measures are equal.

$$m\angle LMF = m\angle KMD = 124° \ \blacksquare$$

EXAMPLE 3

Find the angle measure.

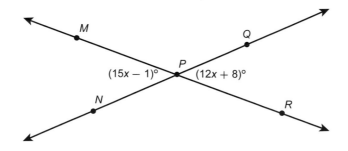

A Find $m\angle QPR$.

SOLUTION

$\angle MPN$ and $\angle QPR$ are vertical angles.

Step 1 Write an equation and solve for x.

$m\angle MPN = m\angle QPR$

$15x - 1 = 12x + 8$	Substitute.
$3x - 1 = 8$	Subtract $12x$ from both sides.
$3x = 9$	Add 1 to both sides.
$x = 3$	Divide each side by 3.

Step 2 Substitute 3 for x in the expression for $m\angle QPR$.

$$m\angle QPR = (12x + 8)^\circ$$
$$= (12(3) + 8)^\circ$$
$$= 44^\circ$$

B Find $m\angle RPN$.

SOLUTION

$\angle RPN$ and $\angle QPR$ are a linear pair, so their angle measures have a sum of 180°.

$$m\angle RPN + m\angle QPR = 180^\circ$$
$$m\angle RPN + 44^\circ = 180^\circ$$
$$m\angle RPN = 136^\circ \ \blacksquare$$

Identifying Complementary and Supplementary Angles

Definitions
A pair of angles is **complementary** if the sum of their measures is 90°.
A pair of angles is **supplementary** if the sum of their measures is 180°.

Complementary and supplementary angle pairs may or may not be adjacent. Points *H*, *M*, and *L* are collinear.

∠*HMJ* and ∠*JMK* are complementary.

∠*HMK* and ∠*KML* are supplementary.

∠*HMJ* and ∠*JML* are supplementary.

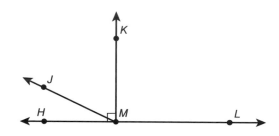

∠*A* and ∠*C* are complementary.

∠*A* and ∠*B* are supplementary.

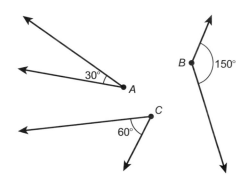

Finding Measures of Complements and Supplements

EXAMPLE 4

Find the measure of the complement and the supplement of an angle with the measure.

A 82°

SOLUTION
The complement has a measure of $90° - 82° = 8°$. The supplement has a measure of $180° - 82° = 98°$.

> ▶ **Think About It** If two angles are supplementary, you can write their measures as x and $180° - x$.

B 105°

SOLUTION
The angle does not have a complement. The supplement has a measure of $180° - 105° = 75°$. ∎

EXAMPLE 5

$\angle A$ and $\angle B$ are complementary angles. The measure of $\angle B$ is twice the measure of $\angle A$. Find the measure of each angle.

SOLUTION
Let $m\angle A = x$. Then $m\angle B = 90° - x$.

Step 1 Write an equation. The measure of $\angle B$ is twice the measure of $\angle A$.

$m\angle B = 2 \cdot m\angle A$

$90° - x = 2x$ Substitute.

$90° = 3x$ Add x to both sides.

$30° = x$ Divide each side by 3.

Step 2 Substitute 30° for x in each expression.

$$m\angle A = x \qquad m\angle B = 90° - x$$
$$= 30° \qquad\qquad = 90° - 30°$$
$$= 60°$$

$$m\angle A = 30° \text{ and } m\angle B = 60° \; \blacksquare$$

Application: Hobbies

EXAMPLE 6

An antique bicycle wheel has only a few spokes remaining. Use the diagram to answer the questions. $\overline{CF}$ and $\overline{AE}$ intersect at center K.

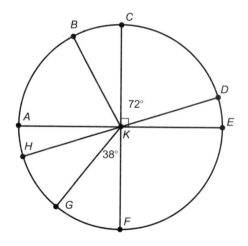

A What is $m\angle HKG$?

SOLUTION

$m\angle HKF = 72°$ because $\angle HKF$ and $\angle CKD$ are vertical angles.

$$m\angle HKG = m\angle HKF - m\angle GKF = 72° - 38° = 34°$$

B What is $m\angle DKF$?

SOLUTION

$\angle CKD$ and $\angle DKF$ are a linear pair.

$$m\angle DKF = 180° - 72° = 108°$$

C Name a pair of supplementary angles that are congruent.

SOLUTION

Angles that are supplementary and congruent each measure 90°. One pair of supplementary congruent angles is $\angle AKC$ and $\angle CKE$. ▪

Parallel Lines and Transversals

Two lines either intersect or do not intersect each other.

▶ **Think About It** Like roads at an intersection, lines can intersect or cross one another.

Parallel lines are lines on the same plane that never intersect. The symbol for parallel is ∥.

$a \parallel b$ is read "line a is parallel to line b."

Line $f \parallel$ line g, but line $e \nparallel$ line f and line $e \nparallel g$ because line e and the other lines are not on the same plane.

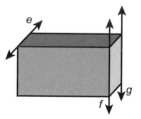

▶ **Think About It** The symbol $\nparallel$ is read "is not parallel to."

A **transversal** is a line that intersects two or more lines in a plane. Line t is a transversal to lines m and n.

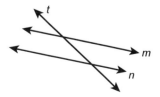

Pairs of Angles

Notice that eight angles are formed when a transversal crosses two lines.

Corresponding angles are angles that lie in the same position or match up with respect to the transversal when the transversal crosses two lines. Pairs of corresponding angles in this figure are ∠1 and ∠5, ∠2 and ∠6, ∠3 and ∠7, and ∠4 and ∠8.

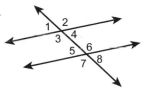

Alternate interior angles are the inside angles that do not share the same vertex and are on opposite sides of a transversal crossing two lines. Pairs of alternate interior angles in this figure are ∠3 and ∠6, as well as ∠4 and ∠5.

Alternate exterior angles are the outside angles that do not share the same vertex and are on opposite sides of a transversal crossing two lines. The alternate exterior angles are the angle pair ∠1 and ∠8 and the angle pair ∠2 and ∠7.

> ▶ **Think About It** interior — inside
> exterior = outside

Adjacent angles are angle pairs with a common side and a common vertex that do not overlap. There are several adjacent angles in the figure, including ∠1 and ∠2, ∠1 and ∠3, ∠3 and ∠4, ∠5 and ∠7, ∠5 and ∠6, and ∠7 and ∠8.

> ▶ **Think About It** ∠ABD and ∠CBD are adjacent angles.
> common side: $\overrightarrow{BD}$
> common vertex: B

EXAMPLE 1

Identify the pair of angles as corresponding, alternate interior, alternate exterior, adjacent, or none of these.

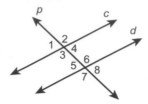

A ∠3 and ∠6

SOLUTION

∠3 and ∠6 are on opposite sides of the transversal, line *p*, and they do not share a vertex. They are in between lines *c* and *d*, so they are alternate interior angles.

B ∠2 and ∠7

SOLUTION

∠2 and ∠7 are on opposite sides of the transversal, line *p*, and they do not share the same vertex. They are outside of lines *c* and *d*, so they are alternate exterior angles.

C ∠5 and ∠6

SOLUTION

∠5 and ∠6 share a common side and a common vertex. They are adjacent angles.

D ∠4 and ∠8

SOLUTION

∠4 and ∠8 are in the same position within their group of four angles. They are corresponding angles. ◾

Finding Angle Measures

▶ **Remember** The letter *m* is used to represent the word *measure*. So *m*∠1 is read as "the measure of angle 1."

The sum of the measures of two adjacent angles equals the measure of the angle formed by the sides that are not common.

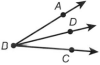

In the figure, $m\angle ABD + m\angle DBC = m\angle ABC$.

If $m\angle ABD = 20°$ and $m\angle DBC = 17°$, then $m\angle ABC = 37°$.

Properties of Special Angle Pairs

When two lines are crossed by a transversal, the sum of the measures of any two adjacent angles is 180°.

When the two lines crossed by the transversal are parallel, the following statements are also true:

- The measures of any pair of corresponding angles are equal.
- The measures of any pair of alternate interior angles are equal.
- The measures of any pair of alternate exterior angles are equal.

EXAMPLE 2

Find the measure of the angle if $j \parallel k$.

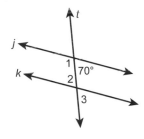

A $m\angle 1$

SOLUTION

$\angle 1$ is adjacent to the 70° angle. Because the sum of these angles is 180°, $m\angle 1 = 180° - 70° = 110°$.

B $m\angle 2$

SOLUTION

$\angle 2$ and the 70° angle are alternate interior angles, so they have the same measure.

$$m\angle 2 = 70°$$

C $m\angle 3$

SOLUTION

$\angle 3$ and the 70° angle are corresponding angles, so they have the same measure.

$$m\angle 3 = 70° \ \blacksquare$$

EXAMPLE 3

Find the measure of the angle if $m\angle 1 = 45°$ and $m \parallel n$.

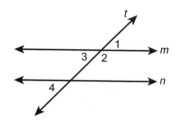

A $m\angle 2$

SOLUTION

$\angle 2$ is adjacent to $\angle 1$, so $m\angle 2 = 180° - 45° = 135°$.

B $m\angle 3$

SOLUTION

$\angle 3$ is adjacent to $\angle 2$, so $m\angle 3 = 180° - 135° = 45°$.

C $m\angle 4$

SOLUTION

$\angle 4$ and $\angle 1$ are alternate exterior angles, so they have the same measure.

$$m\angle 4 = 45° \ \blacksquare$$

Circumference of Circles and Area

Some farmers use irrigation systems that water a circular area for crops. These farmers need to have a sound understanding of area so they know how much water they need, how much seed to plant, and how much crop their land can yield.

Circles

The circle is a common and useful shape.

Definitions

A **circle** is the set of all points in a plane that are equidistant from a given point called the **center**.

▶ **Think About It** *Equidistant* means "the same distance."

Remember that the side of a polygon is a line segment. A circle does not have any sides, so circles are not polygons.

The center of a circle is not part of the circle. It is used to determine which points form the circle. The center point can be used to name the circle.

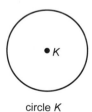

circle *K*

Identifying Radii

Definition

A **radius** of a circle is a segment that connects the center to a point on the circle. The plural of *radius* is *radii*.

radius

EXAMPLE 1

A Name the radii shown for circle *P*.

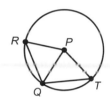

SOLUTION
The radii are $\overline{PR}$, $\overline{PQ}$, and $\overline{PT}$.

▶ **Think About It** Every circle has an infinite number of radii.

B Name the radii shown for circle *A*.

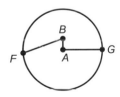

SOLUTION
Because *A* is the center of the circle, $\overline{AG}$ is the only radius shown. ■

Identifying Chords and Diameters

Definitions

A **chord** is a line segment that connects any two points on a circle.

A **diameter** is a chord that contains the center of the circle.

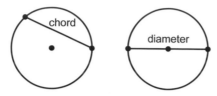

▶ **Think About It** Every circle has an infinite number of diameters and an infinite number of chords.

EXAMPLE 2

A Name the chords shown for circle Q.

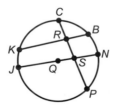

SOLUTION

Look for segments whose endpoints are on the circle. The chords are $\overline{KB}$, $\overline{JN}$, and $\overline{CP}$.

▶ **Think About It** Every diameter is a chord, but not every chord is a diameter.

B Name the diameters shown for circle Q.

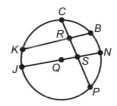

SOLUTION

The only chord shown that passes through the center of the circle is $\overline{JN}$, so $\overline{JN}$ is a diameter of the circle. ■

Calculating a Radius or Diameter

Look again at circle Q in Example 2. Point Q separates the diameter $\overline{JN}$ into two segments of equal length: $\overline{QJ}$ and $\overline{QN}$, which are both radii.

> ## Radius and Diameter Formula
>
> Let d be the diameter of a circle and r be the radius. The diameter d of a circle is twice the radius r of the circle.
>
> $$d = 2r$$

▶ **Think About It** Diameter and radius can each refer to the segment or to the length of the segment. The radius refers to the length. A radius refers to a segment.

EXAMPLE 3

A What is the diameter of circle M?

18 in.

SOLUTION

The radius r is 18 in.

$d = 2r$

$\quad = 2 \cdot 18$ Substitute 18 for r.

$\quad = 36$ Multiply.

The diameter is 36 in.

B Find the radius of a circle that has a diameter of 15 cm.

SOLUTION

Substitute 15 for d and solve for r.

$\quad d = 2r$

$15 = 2r$ Substitute 15 for d.

$\dfrac{15}{2} = r$ Divide both sides by 2.

$7.5 = r$ Simplify.

The radius is 7.5 cm. ∎

Application: Boating

EXAMPLE 4

A lake is approximately circular and has an average diameter of 3265 ft. A small island is located so the dock is at the center of the lake. A tour boat takes people to and from the island several times a day. If the boat travels about 26,120 ft every day, how many one-way trips does the boat make every day?

SOLUTION

The distance from the side of the lake to the island is the radius of the lake.
Find the average radius of the lake.

$$d = 2r$$

3265 $= 2r$ Substitute 3265 for d.

$$\frac{3265}{2} = r$$ Divide both sides by 2.

$$1632.5 = r$$ Simplify.

Divide the total distance the boat travels by the radius to determine how
many one-way trips the boat makes.

$$26{,}120 \div 1632.5 = 16$$

The boat makes 16 one-way trips every day. ■

Circumference

The distance around a polygon is called its perimeter, and the distance around a circle is called its circumference.

Definition
The **circumference** of a circle is the distance around the circle.

Finding the Circumference of a Circle

Since ancient times, people have known that the ratio of the circumference to the diameter of any circle is a constant that is just a bit more than 3. This constant is called π (pi), which is a decimal number that never repeats and never ends. In calculations, it is often approximated as 3.14.

Circumference of a Circle Formula

The circumference of a circle with diameter d and radius r is

$$C = \pi d \text{ or } C = 2\pi r.$$

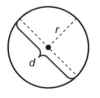

Answers that are found by substituting 3.14 for π are estimates and should include the approximately equal to ($\approx$) symbol. Answers that use the symbol π are exact answers.

> ▶ **Think About It** In a given circle, the diameter is twice the radius, so
> $C = \pi d = \pi 2r = 2\pi r$.

EXAMPLE 1

Find the circumference of the circle. Give both exact and approximate answers.

A circle A

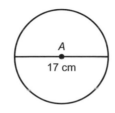

SOLUTION

Because the diameter is given, use $C = \pi d$.

$C = \pi d$	Write the formula.
$= \pi \cdot 17$	Substitute 17 for d.
$\approx 3.14 \cdot 17$	Substitute 3.14 for π.
≈ 53.4	Multiply.

The circumference is exactly 17π cm, or about 53.4 cm.

> ▶ **Think About It** When using 3.14 for π, use three digits when writing the circumference.

B circle with radius of 5 m

SOLUTION

Because the radius is given, use $C = 2\pi r$.

$C = 2\pi r$	Write the formula.
$= 2 \cdot \pi \cdot \mathbf{5}$	Substitute 5 for r.
$= 10\pi$	Multiply.
$\approx 10 \cdot \mathbf{3.14}$	Substitute 3.14 for π.
≈ 31.4	Multiply.

The circumference is exactly 10π m, or about 31.4 m. ■

> ▶ **Think About It** Find the exact answer in terms of π first, and then substitute a value of π to find an approximation.

Finding Missing Lengths

EXAMPLE 2

A The circumference of a circle is 18π ft. What is the radius?

SOLUTION

Substitute the known information into $C = 2\pi r$. Solve for r.

$C = 2\pi r$	Write the formula.
$\mathbf{18\pi} = 2 \cdot \pi \cdot r$	Substitute 18π for C.
$18 = 2r$	Divide both sides by π.
$9 = r$	Divide both sides by 2.

The radius is 9 ft.

B The circumference of a circle is 40 yd. What is the diameter?

SOLUTION

Substitute the known information into $C = \pi d$. Solve for d.

$C = \pi d$ — Write the formula.

$40 = \pi d$ — Substitute 40 for C.

$\dfrac{40}{\pi} = d$ — Divide both sides by π.

$\dfrac{40}{3.14} \approx d$ — Substitute 3.14 for π.

$12.7 \approx d$ — Divide both sides by 3.14.

The diameter is about 12.7 yd. ■

Finding Perimeters of Partial and Combination Figures

A semicircle is half a circle. To find the circumference of a semicircle, divide by 2.

$$C = \frac{\pi d}{2} \text{ or } C = \frac{\overset{1}{2}\pi r}{\underset{1}{2}} = \pi r$$

A quarter circle is one-fourth of a circle. To find the circumference of a quarter circle, divide by 4.

$$C = \frac{\pi d}{4} \text{ or } C = \frac{\overset{1}{2}\pi r}{\underset{2}{4}} = \frac{\pi r}{2}$$

EXAMPLE 3

A Find the exact circumference of a semicircle with radius 5 cm.

SOLUTION

Use the formula $C = \pi r$.

$C = \pi r$ — Use the formula for circumference of a semicircle.

$C = \pi \cdot 5$ — Substitute 5 for r.

$C = 5\pi$ — Simplify.

The exact circumference is 5π cm.

B Find the circumference of a quarter circle with diameter 6 in.
Use 3.14 to approximate π.

SOLUTION

Use the formula $C = \dfrac{\pi d}{4}$.

$C = \dfrac{\pi \cdot 6}{4}$ Subtitute 6 for *d*.

$C = 1.5\pi$ Simplify.

$C \approx 1.5 \cdot \mathbf{3.14}$ Substitute 3.14 for π.

$C \approx 4.71$ Multiply.

The circumference is exactly 1.5π cm, or about 4.71 cm. ◼

EXAMPLE 4

A The figure is made up of two semicircles and a rectangle.
Find the perimeter of the figure.

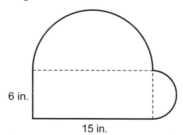

6 in.

15 in.

SOLUTION

$P = \dfrac{\pi d_1}{2} + \dfrac{\pi d_2}{2} + 6 + 15$ Add the circumference of the semicircles to the two sides of the rectangle.

$= \dfrac{\pi \cdot 15}{2} + \dfrac{\pi \cdot 6}{2} + 6 + 15$ Substitute 15 for π*d* and 6 for πd_2.

$= 10.5\pi + 21$ Simplify.

$\approx 10.5 \cdot \mathbf{3.14} + 21$ Substitute 3.14 for π.

≈ 54.0 Simplify.

The perimeter is about 54 in.

B The figure is made up of two congruent squares and a quarter circle. Find the perimeter of the figure to the nearest tenth.

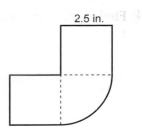

2.5 in.

SOLUTION

The side of each square is the radius of the quarter circle.

$$P = 6s + \frac{\pi r}{2}$$ Add the six sides of the square to the circumference of the quarter circle.

$$= 6 \cdot 2.5 + \frac{\pi \cdot 2.5}{2}$$ Substitute 2.5 for s and r.

$$= 15 + 1.25\pi$$ Simplify.

$$\approx 15 + 1.25 \cdot 3.14$$ Substitute 3.14 for π.

$$\approx 15 + 3.93$$ Multiply.

$$\approx 18.9$$ Add.

The perimeter is about 18.9 in. ■

Application: Sports

EXAMPLE 5

A bicycle wheel has a radius of 16 in. It is rolled on the ground for one complete revolution. How far did the wheel travel?

SOLUTION

The distance traveled equals the circumference of the wheel.

$$C = 2\pi r$$ Write the formula.

$$= 2 \cdot \pi \cdot 16$$ Substitute 16 for r.

$$= 32\pi$$ Multiply.

$$\approx 32 \cdot 3.14$$ Substitute 3.14 for π.

$$\approx 100$$ Multiply.

The wheel traveled about 100 in. ■

Areas of Circles

In addition to its use in the formula for circumference, π can help you calculate the area of a circle.

Finding the Area of a Circle

Area of a Circle Formula

The area of a circle with radius r is

$$A = \pi r^2.$$

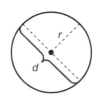

▶ **Think About It** r^2 is read "r squared" and means $r \bullet r$.

EXAMPLE 1

Find the area of the circle. Give both exact and approximate answers.

A circle C

25 mm

C

SOLUTION

Use the formula with $r = 25$.

$A = \pi r^2$	Write the formula.
$= \pi \cdot \mathbf{25}^2$	Substitute 25 for r.
$= 625\pi$	$25^2 = 625$
$\approx 625 \cdot \mathbf{3.14}$	Substitute 3.14 for π.
≈ 1960	Multiply.

The area is exactly 625π mm^2, or about 1960 mm^2.

> ▶ **Think About It** In the area formula, the order of operations tells you that only the radius is squared. Do not square π.

B circle D

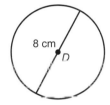

8 cm

D

SOLUTION

The diameter is given. Divide to find the radius: $8 \div 2 = 4$.

$A = \pi r^2$	Write the formula.
$= \pi \cdot \mathbf{4}^2$	Substitute 4 for r.
$= 16\pi$	Simplify.
$\approx 16 \cdot \mathbf{3.14}$	Substitute 3.14 for π.
≈ 50.2	Multiply.

The area is exactly 16π cm^2, or about 50.2 cm^2. ■

Finding Missing Lengths

EXAMPLE 2

A The area of a circle is 100π m^2. What is the radius?

SOLUTION

Substitute the known information into $A = \pi r^2$. Solve for r.

$A = \pi r^2$	Write the formula.
$100\pi = \pi r^2$	Substitute 100π for A.
$100 = r^2$	Divide both sides by π.
$10 = r$	**Think:** What number times itself is 100?

The radius is 10 m.

B The area of a circle is 50 in^2. What is the diameter?

SOLUTION

After solving for r, multiply by 2 to find d.

$A = \pi r^2$	Write the formula.
$50 = \pi \cdot r^2$	Substitute 50 for A.
$\dfrac{50}{\pi} = r^2$	Divide both sides by π.
$\dfrac{50}{3.14} \approx r^2$	Substitute 3.14 for π.
$15.9 \approx r^2$	Divide.
$4 \approx r$	**Think:** $16 = 4 \cdot 4$.

Because the radius is about 4 in., the diameter is about 8 in. ▪

Finding Areas of Partial and Combination Figures

To find the area of a semicircle, divide the formula for the area of a circle by 2.

$$A = \frac{\pi r^2}{2}$$

To find the area of a quarter circle, divide by 4.

$$A = \frac{\pi r^2}{4}$$

EXAMPLE 3

The radius of the semicircle and height of the triangle are shown. Find the area of the figure.

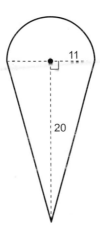

SOLUTION

$A = \dfrac{\pi r^2}{2} + \dfrac{1}{2}bh$	Add the area of the semicircle to the area of the triangle.
$= \dfrac{\pi \cdot 11^2}{2} + \dfrac{1}{2} \cdot 22 \cdot 20$	The base of the triangle is $11 + 11 = 22$.
$= 60.5\pi + 220$	Simplify.
$\approx 60.5 \cdot \mathbf{3.14} + 220$	Substitute 3.14 for π.
$\approx 190 + 220$	Multiply.
≈ 410	Add.

The area is about 410 units^2. ■

Application: Food

EXAMPLE 4

A small pizza has a diameter of 10 in., a medium pizza has a diameter of 13 in., and a large pizza has a diameter of 16 in.

A Estimate the difference in the areas of a medium and large pizza.

▶ **Remember** Divide each diameter by 2 to find each radius.

SOLUTION
Find the area of each pizza.

$$\text{medium: } A = \pi r^2$$
$$= \pi \cdot \mathbf{6.5}^2$$
$$= \pi \cdot 42.25$$
$$\approx \mathbf{3.14} \cdot 42.25$$
$$\approx 133$$

$$\text{large: } A = \pi r^2$$
$$= \pi \cdot \mathbf{8}^2$$
$$= \pi \cdot 64$$
$$\approx \mathbf{3.14} \cdot 64$$
$$\approx 201$$

Subtract to find the difference.

$$201 - 133 = 68$$

The difference is about 68 in^2.

B Angie ate one-fourth of a small pizza. About how many square inches of pizza did she eat?

SOLUTION

Find the area of a quarter circle with a radius of 5 in.

$$A = \frac{\pi r^2}{4}$$ Write the formula.

$$= \frac{\pi \cdot 5^2}{4}$$ Substitute 5 for r.

$$= 6.25\pi$$ Simplify.

$$\approx 6.25 \cdot 3.14$$ Substitute 3.14 for π.

$$\approx 19.6$$ Multiply.

Angie ate about 19.6 in^2 of pizza.

C A pizza with a 14 in. diameter costs $12.95 while a 12 in. pizza costs $10.95. Which pizza is a better deal?

SOLUTION

Find the unit price of each pizza by dividing the cost of the pizza by the area.

$$14 \text{ in. diameter: } A = \pi r^2$$
$$= \pi \cdot 7^2$$
$$\approx 3.14 \cdot 49$$
$$\approx 154$$

$$\text{unit price} \approx \frac{\$12.95}{154 \text{ in}^2}$$
$$\approx \$0.084 \text{ per square inch}$$

$$12 \text{ in. diameter: } A = \pi r^2$$
$$= \pi \cdot 6^2$$
$$\approx 3.14 \cdot 36$$
$$\approx 113$$

$$\text{unit price} \approx \frac{\$10.95}{113 \text{ in}^2}$$
$$\approx \$0.097 \text{ per square inch}$$

The 14 in. pizza is the better deal. ◼

Finding Areas by Subtraction

EXAMPLE 5

Find the area of the shaded region.

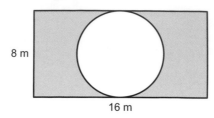

8 m

16 m

SOLUTION

$A = lw - \pi r^2$ Subtract the area of the circle from the area of the rectangle.

$= \mathbf{16} \cdot \mathbf{8} - \pi \cdot \mathbf{4}^2$ Substitute 16 for *l*, 8 for *w*, and 4 for *r*.

$= 128 - 16\pi$ Simplify.

$\approx 128 - 16 \cdot \mathbf{3.14}$ Substitute 3.14 for π.

$\approx 128 - 50.2$ Multiply.

≈ 77.8 Subtract.

The area of the shaded region is about 77.8 m². ■

Circumference and Area

If you know the circumference of a circle, you can calculate its area.

Finding Area from Circumference

Given the circumference of a circle, you can find the circle's area by solving the circumference formula for the radius. Substitute the value of the radius into the formula for the area of the circle and simplify.

> ▶ **Remember** The formula for the circumference of a circle with radius r is $C = 2\pi r$. The formula for the area of a circle with radius r is $A = \pi r^2$.

EXAMPLE 1

Ricki wants to show that the area of a circle with circumference C and radius r is equal to the area of a rectangle with length $\frac{C}{2}$ and width r. How could she show this using a diagram?

SOLUTION

Ricki could draw a circle divided into many equal sectors, and then divide the circle into two equal halves.

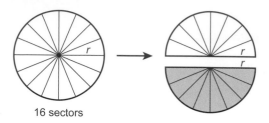

16 sectors

The sectors could be pulled apart and then put back together so that sectors alternate. One sector could be cut in half, and then one of the halves could be moved to form a figure close to the shape of a rectangle.

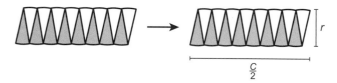

The rectangle has a length of $\frac{C}{2}$ and a width of r, so the area of the rectangle is $A = \frac{C}{2} \cdot r$.

Substituting $C = 2\pi r$ for C into this equation, you get

$$A = \frac{2\pi r}{2} \cdot r = \pi r \cdot r = \pi r^2.$$

Therefore, the area of a rectangle with length $\frac{C}{2}$ and width r is equal to the area of a circle with radius r. ∎

Application: Tiling

EXAMPLE 2

Jaime creates a tiling pattern from 8 blank square tiles, each with a perimeter of 12 cm. He draws circular arcs to define the border of the pattern, then colors in the pattern. What is the area of the colored pattern Jaime created, to the nearest tenth? Explain.

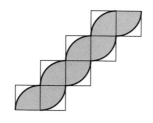

SOLUTION

The circular arc in one tile forms a sector that is one-fourth of a circle with radius 3. The area of this sector is one-fourth of the area A of the complete circle.

The radius of this complete circle is equal to the side length s of the square. You know the perimeter of the square, so you can find s and then solve for A.

Since $4s = 12$, $s = 3$.

$$A = \pi r^2 = \pi(3)^2 = 9\pi$$

The sector area is one-fourth the area of the circle, or $\frac{A}{4}$, which is equal to $\frac{9\pi}{4}$.

> ▸ **Think About It** When simplifying expressions containing π, perform all operations before substituting a numeric value such as 3.14 or $\frac{22}{7}$ for π.

If $\frac{9\pi}{4}$ is the colored-pattern area in one tile and there are 8 tiles in all, then the total colored-pattern area for all 8 tiles is

$$8 \cdot \frac{9\pi}{4} = \frac{8 \cdot 9\pi}{4} = \frac{72\pi}{4} = 18\pi \approx 18 \cdot 3.14 \approx 56.5.$$

The colored-pattern area is about 56.5 cm^2. ∎

Areas of Rectangles and Triangles

Every closed figure has an interior.

The interior of the rectangle is the space enclosed by the sides of the rectangle. The interior of this rectangle is shaded.

Definition

The **area** of a figure is the number of square units in the interior of the figure.

This rectangle has an area of 32 units^2. Notice that 32 is the product of the number of rows, 4, and number of columns, 8.

▶ **Think About It** Area is expressed using square units, such as square feet $\left(\text{ft}^2\right)$. When no units are provided, use square units $\left(\text{units}^2\right)$.

Finding the Area of a Rectangle

Area of a Rectangle Formula

The area of a rectangle with length l and width w is

$$A = lw.$$

EXAMPLE 1

Find the area of the rectangle.

60 mm

11 mm

SOLUTION

Use the formula. The calculation may be performed with or without the units.

Method 1

$A = lw$

$\quad = \mathbf{60 \cdot 11}$ Substitute 60 for l and 11 for w.

$\quad = 660$ Multiply.

Method 2

$A = lw$

$\quad = (60 \text{ mm}) \cdot (11 \text{ mm})$

$\quad = 60 \cdot 11 \cdot \text{mm} \cdot \text{mm}$

$\quad = 660 \text{ mm}^2$

The area is 660 mm^2. ■

▶ **Think About It** Generally use the first method because it is simpler.

Finding the Area of a Triangle

The formula for the area of a triangle is half the formula for the rectangle.

Area of a Triangle Formula

The area of a triangle with base b and height h is

$$A = \frac{1}{2}bh.$$

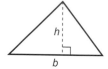

The base of a triangle always forms a right angle with the height of the triangle.

For acute triangles, the height is always shown inside the triangle.
For obtuse triangles, height can be shown in the exterior of the triangle.
In a right triangle, the height can be one of the sides of the triangle.

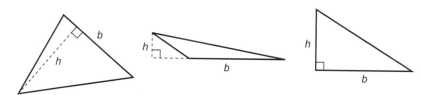

▶ **Think About It** Any side can be used as the base. The height will change accordingly.

EXAMPLE 2

Find the area of the triangle.

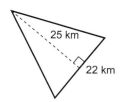

25 km

22 km

SOLUTION

Use the formula.

$A = \frac{1}{2}bh$

$\quad = \frac{1}{2} \cdot 22 \cdot 25$ Substitute 22 for b and 25 for h.

$\quad = 11 \cdot 25$ Multiply.

$\quad = 275$ Multiply.

The area is 275 km^2. ■

Finding Missing Lengths

EXAMPLE 3

A The area of the triangle is 54 cm^2. What is the height of the triangle?

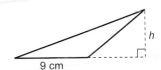

9 cm

SOLUTION

Substitute the known information into $A = \frac{1}{2}bh$. Solve for h.

$A = \frac{1}{2}bh$ Write the formula.

$54 = \frac{1}{2} \cdot 9 \cdot h$ Substitute 54 for A and 9 for b.

$54 = 4.5h$ Simplify.

$12 = h$ Divide both sides by 4.5.

The height is 12 cm.

B The area of a rectangle is 231 in^2. What is the length of the rectangle if the width is 42 in.?

SOLUTION

Substitute the known information into $A = lw$. Solve for l.

$A = lw$	Write the formula.
$231 = l \cdot 42$	Substitute 231 for A and 42 for w.
$5.5 = l$	Divide both sides by 42.

The length is 5.5 in. ■

Finding Areas of Combination Figures

EXAMPLE 4

Find the area of the figure.

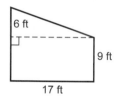

SOLUTION

Add the area of the triangle to the area of the rectangle. The base of the right triangle is the length of the rectangle, 17 ft.

$A = \frac{1}{2}bh + lw$	Use the formulas for area of a triangle and area of a rectangle.
$= \frac{1}{2} \cdot 17 \cdot 6 + 17 \cdot 9$	Substitute 17 for b and l, 6 for h, and 9 for w.
$= 51 + 153$	Multiply.
$= 204$	Add.

The area is 204 ft^2. ■

Finding the Difference of Areas

EXAMPLE 5

Find the area of the shaded portion of the square.

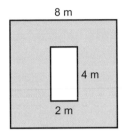

8 m

4 m

2 m

▶ **Remember** The formula for the area of a square is s^2.

SOLUTION

Subtract the area of the rectangle from the area of the square.

$A = s^2 - lw$ Use the formulas for area of a square and area of a rectangle.

$= 8^2 - 2 \cdot 4$ Substitute 8 for s, 2 for l, and 4 for w.

$= 64 - 8$ Simplify.

$= 56$ Subtract.

The area of the shaded region is 56 m^2. ■

Areas of Special Quadrilaterals

Two types of special quadrilaterals are parallelograms and trapezoids. In a parallelogram, both pairs of sides are parallel; in a trapezoid, only one pair of sides is parallel.

Parallelograms and trapezoids have bases and heights. A **base** is defined as the bottom side of a geometric figure. The **height** is perpendicular to the base. It is the length of the segment that extends from the base to the opposite side.

Finding the Area of a Parallelogram

Every parallelogram has four bases; each side can be a base. The height depends on which side is used as the base. Heights are sometimes shown outside the parallelogram.

Area of a Parallelogram Formula

The area of a parallelogram with base b and height h is

$$A = bh.$$

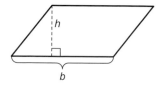

> ▶ **Think About It** Any side of a parallelogram can be the base because the parallelogram can be rotated so that any side is on the bottom.

EXAMPLE 1

Find the area of the parallelogram.

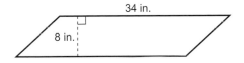

SOLUTION

$A = bh$	Write the formula.
$= 34 \cdot 8$	Substitute 34 for b and 8 for h.
$- 272$	Multiply.

The area is 272 in^2. ■

Finding the Area of a Trapezoid

A trapezoid has two bases: b_1 and b_2. The parallel sides are always the bases. The height is the length of a segment that joins the bases and forms right angles with them.

Area of a Trapezoid Formula

The area of a trapezoid with bases b_1 and b_2 and height h is

$$A = \frac{1}{2}h(b_1 + b_2).$$

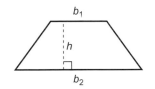

EXAMPLE 2

Find the area of the trapezoid.

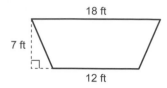

18 ft

7 ft

12 ft

SOLUTION

$A = \frac{1}{2}h(b_1 + b_2)$ Write the formula.

$= \frac{1}{2} \cdot 7 \cdot (18 + 12)$ Substitute 18 for b_1, 12 for b_2, and 7 for h.

$= \frac{1}{2} \cdot 7 \cdot 30$ Simplify inside the parentheses.

$= 105$ Multiply.

The area is 105 ft^2. ■

▶ **Think About It** It does not matter which base is used for b_1 and which is used for b_2.

Finding Missing Lengths

With a known area and some algebra, you can find missing side lengths.

EXAMPLE 3

Find the missing side length.

A The area of a parallelogram is 675 cm^2. What is the height of the parallelogram if its base is 45 cm long?

SOLUTION

Substitute the known information into $A = bh$. Solve for h.

$A = bh$ Write the formula.

$675 = 45 \cdot h$ Substitute 675 for A and 45 for b.

$15 = h$ Divide both sides by 45.

The height is 15 cm.

B The area of the trapezoid is 54 m. What is the base length?

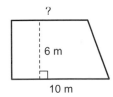

SOLUTION

$A = \frac{1}{2}h(b_1 + b_2)$ Write the formula.

$54 = \frac{1}{2} \cdot 6 \cdot (b_1 + 10)$ Substitute 54 for A, 6 for h, and 10 for one of the bases.

$54 = 3 \cdot (b_1 + 10)$ Multiply on the right.

$18 = b_1 + 10$ Divide both sides by 3.

$8 = b_1$ Subtract 10 from both sides.

CHECK

$$A = \frac{1}{2}h(b_1 + b_2) = \frac{1}{2} \cdot 6 \cdot (8 + 10) = 3 \cdot 18 = 54 \checkmark$$

The length of the unknown base is 8 m. ■

Application: Painting

EXAMPLE 4

Each wall of a four-sided garden shed is 10 ft long and 8 ft high and has one rhombus-shaped window. The windows are congruent and each has a base of 2 ft and a height of 1.5 ft. The gardener wants to paint the inside of the walls. A can of the paint covers about 350 ft^2/gal. How many cans of paint will she need for 2 coats?

▶ **Think About It** A rhombus is a parallelogram with four equal sides. A square is one example of a rhombus.

SOLUTION

Find the area to be painted.

First find the area that is covered with 1 coat.

$A = 4lw - 4bh$	Subtract the area of the windows from the area of the walls.
$= 4 \cdot 10 \cdot 8 - 4 \cdot 2 \cdot 1.5$	Substitute values for the variables.
$= 320 - 12$	Multiply.
$= 308$	Subtract.

She has to cover 308 ft^2 with 1 coat.

▶ **Think About It** You can also use $A = 4(lw - bh)$.

Next double that amount to find the area covered in 2 coats.

$2 \times 308 = 616$ Multiply the area covered by 1 coat by 2.

Divide by 350 to find how many cans of paint she needs.

$616 \div 350 = 1.76$ Divide by 350.

The gardener will need 2 cans of paint. ■

Three-Dimensional Geometry

Topic List

Many shipping containers are shaped like boxes (rectangular prisms), with consistent volume and surface area. People who have to fill, move, or even paint these containers need to understand volume and surface area.

Slicing Solids

The intersection of a plane and a solid often creates a recognizable two-dimensional shape.

Finding Cross Sections

Definition
A **cross section** is a plane figure that results from the intersection of a plane and a solid.

The shape of a cross section depends on the shape of the solid and the angle of the slice.

EXAMPLE 1

Find the cross section of the right rectangular prism and a plane parallel to its base.

▶ **Remember** The base of a right rectangular prism is a rectangle.

SOLUTION

The plane slices through the right rectangular prism horizontally, creating a rectangle parallel to the base. This rectangle is congruent to the base of the prism.

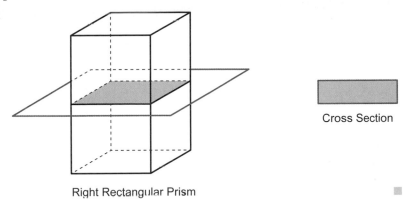

Right Rectangular Prism

Cross Section

EXAMPLE 2

Find the cross section of the right rectangular pyramid and a plane perpendicular to its base. The plane passes through the pyramid's vertex.

SOLUTION

The plane slices through the right rectangular pyramid vertically, creating a triangle perpendicular to the base of the pyramid. The triangle is isosceles, with height equal to the height of the pyramid.

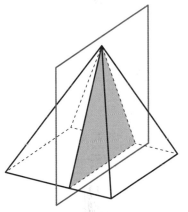

Right Rectangular Pyramid

Cross Section

EXAMPLE 3

Find the cross section of the cone and a plane parallel to its base.

SOLUTION

The plane slices through the cone horizontally, creating a circle parallel to the base of the cone. The closer the plane is to the base, the larger the diameter of the circular cross section.

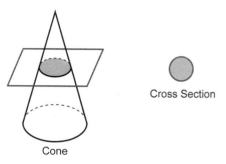

Cross Section

Cone

EXAMPLE 4

Find the cross section of the right cylinder and the plane. The plane is neither parallel nor perpendicular to the cylinder's base.

SOLUTION

If the plane slicing the cylinder were parallel to the base, the cross section would be a circle. However, the plane slicing the cylinder is not parallel to the base and does not intersect either base. So the cross section is in the shape of an ellipse.

▶ **Remember** An ellipse looks like a circle that is stretched, or elongated, either vertically or horizontally.

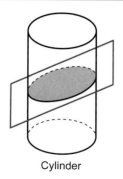

Cross Section

Cylinder

Surface Area

The surface area of a figure is the sum of the areas of each of its faces (including bases).

Finding the Surface Area of a Cube

A cube has six congruent square faces. If each square face has side length s, then the area of each one is s^2. The surface area of a cube with side length s is $6 \cdot s^2$.

Surface Area of a Cube Formula

The formula for the surface area of a cube with side s is

$$SA = 6s^2.$$

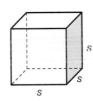

EXAMPLE 1

Find the surface area of the cube.

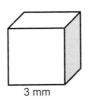

3 mm

▶ **Remember** Area is measured in square units.

SOLUTION

The length *s* of each side is 3 mm.

$SA = 6s^2$ Write the surface area formula.

$\quad = 6 \cdot 3^2$ Substitute for *s*.

$\quad = 6 \cdot 9$ Evaluate the power.

$\quad = 54$ Multiply.

The surface area of the cube is 54 mm^2. ■

Finding the Lateral Area of a Prism

The **lateral area** of a figure is the sum of the areas of its lateral faces only. One way to find the lateral area is to find the area of each lateral face, and then add. Or you can use a formula.

Lateral Area of a Prism Formula

The formula for the lateral area of a prism with perimeter *P* and height *h* is

$$LA = Ph.$$

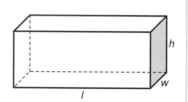

▶ **Remember** The perimeter of a rectangle with length *l* and width *w* is

$$2l + 2w.$$

EXAMPLE 2

A Find the lateral area of the rectangular prism by adding the areas of its lateral faces. Assume the figure is resting on its base.

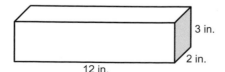

12 in.

3 in.

2 in.

> ▶ **Think About It** With a rectangular prism, any of the faces could be the base.

SOLUTION

The four lateral faces are the front, right side, back, and left sides of the prism.

area of front: $12 \times 3 = 36$ area of back: $12 \times 3 = 36$

area of right side: $2 \times 3 = 6$ area of left side: $2 \times 3 = 6$

lateral area $= 36 \text{ in}^2 + 36 \text{ in}^2 + 6 \text{ in}^2 + 6 \text{ in}^2 = 84 \text{ in}^2$

B Find the lateral area of the rectangular prism using the formula. Assume the figure is resting on its base.

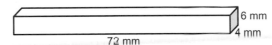

6 mm
4 mm
72 mm

SOLUTION

Find the perimeter P of the base.

$P = 2l + 2w$ Write the perimeter of a rectangle formula.

$= 2 \cdot 72 + 2 \cdot 4$ Substitute 72 for l and 4 for w.

$= 144 + 8$ Multiply.

$= 152$ Add.

Substitute P and h in the formula for lateral area.

$LA = Ph$ Write the lateral area formula.

$= 152 \cdot 6$ Substitute for P and h.

$= 912$ Multiply.

The lateral area of the figure is 912 mm^2. ■

One way to find the **surface area of a rectangular prism** is to find the lateral area and the area of each base, and then add. Or you can use a formula.

Surface Area of a Rectangular Prism Formula

The formula for the surface area of a rectangular prism with base area B, perimeter of the base P, and height h is

$$SA = 2B + LA = 2B + Ph$$

$$= 2lw + 2lh + 2hw.$$

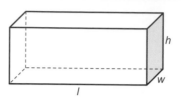

Finding the Surface Area of a Prism

EXAMPLE 3

A Find the surface area of the rectangular prism by adding the areas of its lateral faces and bases.

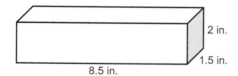

SOLUTION

The four lateral faces are the front, right side, back, and left side of the prism.

area of front: $8.5 \times 2 = 17$ area of back: $8.5 \times 2 = 17$

area of right side: $1.5 \times 2 = 3$ area of left side: $1.5 \times 2 = 3$

area of top: $8.5 \times 1.5 = 12.75$ area of bottom: $8.5 \times 1.5 = 12.75$

$$\text{surface area} = 2 \cdot \left(17 \text{ in}^2\right) + 2 \cdot \left(3 \text{ in}^2\right) + 2 \cdot \left(12.75 \text{ in}^2\right)$$

$$= 34 \text{ in}^2 + 6 \text{ in}^2 + 25.5 \text{ in}^2 = 65.5 \text{ in}^2$$

B Find the surface area of the rectangular prism using the formula.

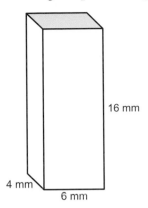

16 mm

4 mm

6 mm

SOLUTION

Find the base area.

$B = lw$ Write the area of a rectangle formula.

$\quad = 4 \cdot 6$ Substitute 4 for l and 6 for w.

$\quad = 24$ Simplify.

Find the perimeter of the base.

$P = 2l + 2w$ Write the perimeter of a rectangle formula.

$\quad = 2 \cdot 4 + 2 \cdot 6$ Substitute 4 for l and 6 for w.

$\quad = 8 + 12$ Multiply.

$\quad = 20$ Add.

Plug B, P, and h into the formula for surface area.

> ▶ **Think About It** Finding B, P, and h before substituting into the surface area formula can help you avoid mistakes.

$SA = 2B + Ph$ Write the surface area formula.

$\quad = 2 \cdot 24 + 20 \cdot 16$ Substitute for B, P, and h.

$\quad = 48 + 320$ Multiply.

$\quad = 368$ Add.

The surface area of the figure is 368 mm^2.

C Fiona needs to know the surface area of a box so she can purchase enough wrapping paper to cover it. Find the surface area of the box using the formula.

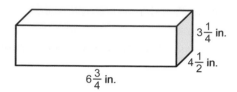

$3\frac{1}{4}$ in.

$4\frac{1}{2}$ in.

$6\frac{3}{4}$ in.

SOLUTION

Find the base area.

$B = lw$ Write the area of a rectangle formula.

$= 6\frac{3}{4} \cdot 4\frac{1}{2}$ Substitute $6\frac{3}{4}$ for l and $4\frac{1}{2}$ for w.

$= \frac{27}{4} \cdot \frac{9}{2}$ Rewrite the mixed numbers as improper fractions.

$= \frac{243}{8}$ Multiply.

$= 30\frac{3}{8}$ Simplify.

Find the perimeter of the base.

$P = 2l + 2w$ Write the perimeter of a rectangle formula.

$= 2 \cdot 6\frac{3}{4} + 2 \cdot 4\frac{1}{2}$ Substitute $6\frac{3}{4}$ for l and $4\frac{1}{2}$ for w.

$= 2 \cdot \frac{27}{4} + 2 \cdot \frac{9}{2}$ Rewrite the mixed numbers as improper fractions.

$= \frac{27}{2} + \frac{9}{1}$ Multiply.

$= \frac{45}{2}$ Add.

$= 22\frac{1}{2}$ Simplify.

Plug B, P, and h into the formula for surface area.

$SA = 2B + Ph$ Write the surface area formula.

$= 2 \cdot 30\frac{3}{8} + 22\frac{1}{2} \cdot 3\frac{1}{4}$ Substitute for B, P, and h.

$= 2 \cdot \frac{243}{8} + \frac{45}{2} \cdot \frac{13}{4}$ Rewrite the mixed numbers as improper fractions.

$= \frac{486}{8} + \frac{585}{8}$ Multiply.

$= \frac{1071}{8}$ Add.

$= 133\frac{7}{8}$ Simplify.

The surface area of the box is $133\frac{7}{8}$ in^2. ■

Finding the Surface Area of a Complex Figure

EXAMPLE 4

Find the surface area of the figure.

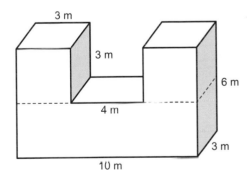

SURFACE AREA **289**

SOLUTION

The figure is a rectangular prism topped with two congruent cubes. Find the sum of the surface areas of the three figures, then subtract the area where the figures meet.

▶ **Think About It** You could also find the surface area of the figure by adding the areas of each face.

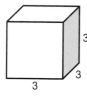 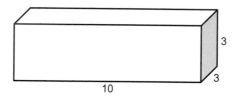

$SA = 6s^2$

$\quad = 6 \cdot 3^2$

$\quad = 6 \cdot 9$

$\quad = 54$

$SA = 6s^2$

$\quad = 6 \cdot 3^2$

$\quad = 6 \cdot 9$

$\quad = 54$

$SA = 2B + Ph$

$\quad = 2 \cdot (10 \cdot 3) + (2 \cdot 10 + 2 \cdot 3) \cdot 3$

$\quad = 2 \cdot 30 + 26 \cdot 3$

$\quad = 60 + 78$

$\quad = 138$

The total surface area of the figures is $54 \text{ m}^2 + 54 \text{ m}^2 + 138 \text{ m}^2 = 246 \text{ m}^2$.

Subtract the area of the bottom face of each cube and the areas on the top of the rectangular prism where the figures meet.

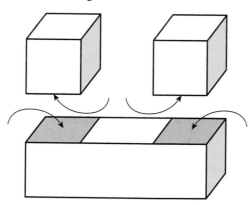

$246 - 4 \cdot 3^2 = 246 - 4 \cdot 9$ For each square surface, use $s = 3$ m.

$\qquad = 246 - 36$ Multiply.

$\qquad = 210$ Subtract.

The surface area of the figure is 210 m^2. ■

Volume

Volume is a way to measure a three-dimensional object.

A **cube** is a solid figure made up of 6 square faces that meet each other at right angles. A cube has 8 vertices and 12 edges. The length, width, and height of a cube are equal.

Counting to Find the Volume of a Cube

The **volume** of a three-dimensional figure is a measure of the space inside the figure. You find volume by determining the number of cubes needed to fill a figure. Volume is measured in **cubic units**.

EXAMPLE 1

Find the volume of the cube.

4 cm

SOLUTION

Fill the cube with centimeter cubes.

Place 4 rows of 4 cubes on the bottom.

$4 \times 4 = 16$

The first layer holds 16 centimeter cubes.

Make 4 layers of 16 cubes.

$4 \times 16 = 64$

The figure holds 64 centimeter cubes.

The volume of the cube is 64 cubic centimeters, or 64 cm^3. ■

Using a Formula to Find the Volume of a Cube

You can use a formula to find the volume of a cube.

Volume of a Cube Formula
The formula for the volume of a cube with side s is $$V = s \cdot s \cdot s = s^3.$$ 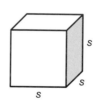

▶ **Think About It** When calculating volume, it is easier to calculate without the units, then add them in the final answer. But you can certainly include the units in your calculations. However you do it, be careful with your units.

EXAMPLE 2

Find the volume of the cube.

 A

12 cm

SOLUTION

$V = s^3$ Write the volume formula.

$= 12^3$ Substitute 12 for s.

$= 1728$ Evaluate the power.

The volume is 1728 cm^3.

B

8 ft

SOLUTION

$V = s^3$ Write the volume formula.

$= 8^3$ Substitute 8 for s.

$= 512$ Evaluate the power.

The volume is 512 ft^3. ■

EXAMPLE 3

Ali has two fish tanks. The smaller tank is a cube with a side 15 in. long, and the larger tank is a cube with a side 20 in. long. Find the volume of both fish tanks. What is the difference in volume between the two fish tanks?

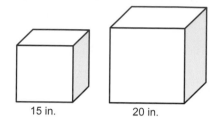

15 in.   20 in.

SOLUTION

Step 1 Find the volume of the smaller fish tank.

$V = s^3$ Write the volume formula.

$= 15^3$ Substitute 15 for s.

$= 3375$ Evaluate the power.

The volume of the smaller fish tank is 3375 in^3.

Step 2 Find the volume of the larger fish tank.

$V = s^3$ Write the volume formula.

$= 20^3$ Substitute 20 for s.

$= 8000$ Evaluate the power.

The volume of the larger fish tank is 8000 in^3.

Step 3 Find the difference in volume of the tanks by subtracting the volume of the smaller tank from the volume of the larger tank.

$$8000 - 3375 = 4625$$

The volume of the larger tank is 4625 in^3 greater than the volume of the smaller tank. ■

Volumes of Prisms

Many real-world containers have the shape of a prism. Calculating the capacity tells you how much the container can hold.

Identifying Parts of Prisms

A **prism** is a solid figure with parallel congruent **bases** that are both polygons. The **lateral faces** are all parallelograms. The name of a prism comes from the shape of its bases.

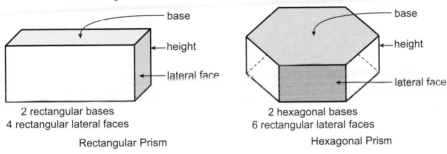

2 rectangular bases
4 rectangular lateral faces

Rectangular Prism

2 hexagonal bases
6 rectangular lateral faces

Hexagonal Prism

▶ **Think About It** Think of the bases of a prism as its floor and ceiling. Think of the lateral faces as walls. But watch out! A prism does not always sit on one of its bases. Sometimes it sits on a lateral face, as in Examples 1B and 1C.

EXAMPLE 1

Name the prism. Give the shape of its bases and the number of lateral faces.

A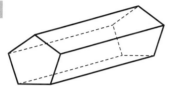

SOLUTION

The bases are rectangles. There are four lateral faces. The figure is a rectangular prism.

B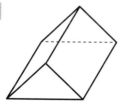

SOLUTION

The bases are pentagons. There are five lateral faces. The figure is a pentagonal prism.

C

SOLUTION

The bases are triangles. There are three lateral faces. The figure is a triangular prism. ■

Computing the Volume of a Prism

Volume of a Prism Formula

The formula for the volume of a prism with base area B and height h is

$$V = Bh.$$

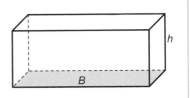

EXAMPLE 2

Find the volume of the prism.

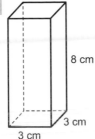

A 8 cm

3 cm

3 cm

SOLUTION

The figure is a square prism.

Step 1 Find B.

$B = s^2$ Write the area of a square formula.

$\quad = 3^2$ Substitute the side length of the square.

$\quad = 9$ Simplify.

The area B of the base of the square prism is 9 cm^2.

Step 2 Find V. The area of the base is 9 cm^2. Use the value for B in the formula.

$V = Bh$ Write the volume formula.

$ = \mathbf{9 \cdot 8}$ Substitute the base area for B and the prism height for h.

$ = 72$ Multiply.

The volume of the square prism is 72 cm^3.

> ▶ **Think About It** For a rectangular prism,
>
> $$B = lw, \text{ so } V = Bh = lwh.$$
>
> Another way to find the volume is to use the formula $V = lwh$.
>
> $$V = lwh$$
> $$= 3 \times 3 \times 8$$
> $$= 72$$

B

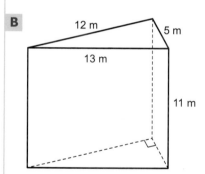

> ▶ **Think About It** Do a separate calculation to find B, using the appropriate area formula.

SOLUTION

The figure is a triangular prism. Use the formula $A = \frac{1}{2}bh$ to find the area of base B.

Step 1 Find B.

$B = \frac{1}{2}bh$ Write the area of a triangle formula.

$ = \frac{1}{2} \cdot 5 \cdot 12$ Substitute the base and height of the triangle.

$ = 30$ Multiply.

The area B of the base of the triangular prism is 30 m^2.

Step 2 Find V. Use the value for B in the formula $V = Bh$.

$V = Bh$ Write the volume formula.

$ = 30 \cdot 11$ Substitute the base area for B and the prism height for h.

$ = 330$ Multiply.

The volume of the triangular prism is 330 m^3.

 C

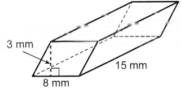

3 mm

15 mm

8 mm

SOLUTION

The figure is a prism with parallelograms as bases. Use the formula $A = bh$ to find the area of base B.

Step 1 Find B.

$B = bh$ Write the area of a parallelogram formula.

$ = 8 \cdot 3$ Substitute the base and height of the parallelogram.

$ = 24$ Multiply.

The area B of the base of the prism is 24 mm^2.

Step 2 Find V. Use the value for B in the formula $V = Bh$.

$V = Bh$ 　　　　Write the volume formula.

$\quad = 24 \cdot 15$ 　　Substitute the base area for B and the prism height for h.

$\quad = 360$ 　　　　Multiply.

The volume of the prism is 360 mm^3. ■

EXAMPLE 3

Xavier has two blocks of clay. He wants to use the block with the greater volume to create a sculpture. Both blocks are rectangular prisms. Find the volumes of the blocks and determine which one has the greater volume.

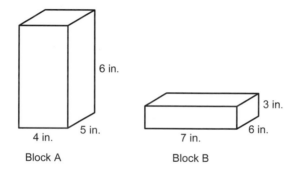

Block A 　　　　　　Block B

SOLUTION

Step 1 Find the volume of Block A.

Find B.

$B = lw$ 　　　　Write the area of a rectangle formula.

$\quad = 4 \cdot 5$ 　　Substitute the length and width of the rectangle.

$\quad = 20$ 　　　　Multiply.

The area B of the base of Block A is 20 in^2.

Find V. Use the value of B in the formula $V = Bh$.

$V = Bh$ 　　　　Write the volume formula.

$\quad = 20 \cdot 6$ 　　Substitute the base area for B and the prism height for h.

$\quad = 120$ 　　　　Multiply.

The volume of Block A is 120 in^3.

Step 2 Find the volume of Block B.

Find B.

$B = lw$ Write the area of a rectangle formula.

   $= 7 \cdot 6$ Substitute the length and width of the rectangle.

   $= 42$ Multiply.

The area B of the base of Block B is 42 in^2.

Find V. Use the value of B in the formula $V = Bh$.

$V = Bh$ Write the volume formula.

   $= 42 \cdot 3$ Substitute the base area for B and the prism height for h.

   $= 126$ Multiply.

The volume of Block B is 126 in^3.

Step 3 Compare the volumes.

$$126 \text{ in}^3 > 120 \text{ in}^3$$

The volume of Block B is greater than the volume of Block A. ▪

Properties of Volume and Surface Area

A solid figure's surface area and volume change when the figure's dimensions change.

Measuring Figures with Different Units

EXAMPLE 1

The surface area of a cube is 150 cm^2. What would change if the surface area of the cube were measured in square meters?

> ▶ **Think About It** The length of a rope does not change when the length is measured with different units. But the number does change. A rope 1 m long also is 100 cm long.
>
> $$1 \text{ m} = 100 \text{ cm}$$

SOLUTION

The surface area does not change. A square meter is larger than a square centimeter, so the number would decrease.

The number representing the surface area would decrease. ▪

EXAMPLE 2

The volume of a cube is 125 cm^3. What would change if the volume of the cube were measured in cubic millimeters?

SOLUTION

The volume does not change. A cubic millimeter is smaller than a cubic centimeter, so the number would increase.

The number representing the volume would increase. ■

Finding Surface Area with Scaled Figures

If you know the surface area or volume of a figure and the scale factor between it and its scaled image, you can use a formula to find the surface area or volume of the scaled image.

▶ **Think About It** A scaled image is an enlarged or a reduced image of a figure.

Definition

A **scale factor** is a ratio of one measure to another. A scale factor greater than 1 enlarges a figure, and a scale factor less than 1 reduces a figure.

Scale Factor Formula

If SA_F is the surface area of a figure that is enlarged or reduced with a scale factor, then the surface area of the scaled image SA_I is

$$SA_I = (\text{scale factor})^2 \cdot SA_F.$$

EXAMPLE 3

Find the surface area of a figure that is an enlargement of a prism with surface area of 160 cm^2. Use a scale factor of 2.

SOLUTION

$SA_I = (\text{scale factor})^2 \cdot SA_F$ Write the scale factor formula.

$\quad = 2^2 \cdot 160$ Replace scale factor with 2 and SA_F with 160.

$\quad = 640$ Simplify.

CHECK

The figure is an enlargement. The figure's surface area should be greater than the original prism's surface area.

$$640 > 160 \checkmark$$

The surface area of the enlargement is 640 cm^2. ■

Finding Figures with the Same Volume but Different Surface Areas

You can use factoring and multiplication properties to find figures that have the same volume but different surface areas.

EXAMPLE 4

Find the dimensions of two rectangular prisms, each with a volume of 48 m^3, but each with a different surface area.

SOLUTION

Write the volume 48 as the product of three numbers two different ways. Use the factors as dimensions of the prisms.

$$V = 48 = 6 \cdot 4 \cdot 2 \qquad\qquad V = 48 = 2 \cdot 3 \cdot 8$$
$$= l_1 w_1 h_1 \qquad\qquad\qquad = l_2 w_2 h_2$$

Find the surface area of each prism.

$$SA_1 = (6 \cdot 2) + (4 \cdot 2) + (6 \cdot 4) + (6 \cdot 2) + (4 \cdot 2) + (6 \cdot 4)$$
$$= 12 + 8 + 24 + 12 + 8 + 24$$
$$= 88$$

$$SA_2 = (2 \cdot 8) + (3 \cdot 8) + (2 \cdot 3) + (2 \cdot 8) + (3 \cdot 8) + (2 \cdot 3)$$
$$= 16 + 24 + 6 + 16 + 24 + 6$$
$$= 92$$

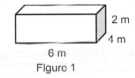

2 m
4 m
6 m
Figure 1

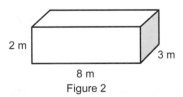

2 m
3 m
8 m
Figure 2

Rectangular prisms with dimensions of 6 m × 4 m × 2 m and 2 m × 3 m × 8 m have the same volume of 48 m^3 but different surface areas. ▪

Statistics

Topic List

Data are everywhere. When you look at a group of people, you could use many numbers to describe them. How tall are they? How long is their hair? How old are they? What is their gender? What color are their eyes? Statistics help you make sense of data.

Measures of Center

A measure of center is a single number used to describe the typical value in a data set.

There are three types of measures of center: mean, median, and mode. They are measures of center because they describe what the "center" or middle of the data looks like.

Mean

The mean is the average of the data. It is found by dividing the sum of the values by the number of values. The mean is often denoted by $\bar{x}$.

> ### ▶ Think About It
> **NOTATION** The symbol $\bar{x}$ is pronounced "x bar."

Definition

The **mean** is the sum of the values in a data set divided by the number of values.

$$\bar{x} = \frac{x_1 + x_2 + \ldots + x_n}{n}$$

EXAMPLE 1

Find the mean of the data set. Round to the nearest tenth.

A $\{8, 9, 2, 3, 0, 6\}$

SOLUTION

$\bar{x} = \dfrac{8 + 9 + 2 + 3 + 0 + 6}{6}$ Use the formula for mean.

$= \dfrac{28}{6} \approx 4.7$ Add the data values and divide by the number of data values.

The mean is about 4.7.

> ▶ **Think About It** Although a value of 0 does not increase the sum of the values in the numerator, it is still counted as a data value in the denominator.

B $\{100, 125, 111, 132, 151\}$

SOLUTION

$\bar{x} = \dfrac{100 + 125 + 111 + 132 + 151}{5}$ Use the formula for mean.

$= \dfrac{619}{5} = 123.8$ Add the data values and divide by the number of data values.

The mean is 123.8.

C $\{-3, -3, -2, 0, 4, 6\}$

SOLUTION

$\bar{x} = \dfrac{-3 + (-3) + (-2) + 0 + 4 + 6}{6}$ Use the formula for mean.

$= \dfrac{2}{6} \approx 0.3$ Add the data values and divide by the number of data values.

The mean is about 0.3. ■

Median

Definition

The **median** is the middle value of a data set after the values have been ordered from least to greatest.

- In a set of data ordered from least to greatest with an odd number of values, the median is the center value.

- In a set of data ordered from least to greatest with an even number of values, the median is the average of the two center values.

▶ **Think About It** Both the mean and the median can be values that do not appear in the data set.

To find the median for an odd number of values, such as 22, 42, 13, 12, and 8, do the following:

Step 1 Arrange the data in order from least to greatest.

$$8, 12, \text{⑬}, 22, 42$$

Step 2 Find the middle number. The number 13 is in the middle. The median is 13.

To find the median for an even number of values, such as 6, 2, 0, 4, 7, and 12, do the following:

Step 1 Arrange the data in order from least to greatest.

$$0, 2, \text{④, ⑥}, 7, 12$$

Step 2 Find the middle numbers. Both 4 and 6 are in the middle.

Step 3 Find the mean of 4 and 6.

$$\frac{4+6}{2} = \frac{10}{2} = 5 \qquad \text{The median is 5.}$$

EXAMPLE 2

Find the median of the set of data.

A hourly wages: $8.50, $7.25, $6.75, $10.00, $9.80

SOLUTION
Arrange the data in order.

$$\$6.75, \$7.25, \$8.50, \$9.80, \$10.00$$

There are five values, so the median is the third one.

The median wage is $8.50.

B height of plant (in centimeters) after 2 wk: 1.7, 1.0, 1.7, 2.4, 3.2, 1.8

SOLUTION
Arrange the data in order.

$$1.0, 1.7, 1.7, 1.8, 2.4, 3.2$$

$\dfrac{1.7 + 1.8}{2} = 1.75$ There are six values, so the median is the average of the third and fourth values.

The median height is 1.75 cm. ∎

Mode

Definition
The **mode** is the data value that occurs the most. If all values occur the same number of times, there is no mode. If two values appear the same number of times, there are two modes.

EXAMPLE 3

Find the mode.

A Find the mode of the values: 7, 4, 2, 2, 4, 7, 9, 7.

SOLUTION
The number 2 occurs twice, 4 occurs twice, 7 occurs 3 times, and 9 occurs once. The mode is 7.

B Test scores are 78, 65, 23, 78, and 42. What is the mode?

SOLUTION
The value 78 occurs twice. All other values occur once. The mode is 78. ▪

Identifying the Best Measure of Center

The mean, median, and mode can all be used to describe a data set. Sometimes one measure of center might be a better description than another. For example, the mean, median, and mode of 22, 31, 40, 210, and 31 are as follows:

The mean is 66.8.   The median is 31.   The mode is 31.

Notice the mean is much different from the median and mode. When extreme values occur in a data set, they can pull the mean far away from most of the data values in the set. An extreme value is called an outlier.

Definition
An **outlier** is a value that is far from the rest of the data.

EXAMPLE 4

Find the mean, median, and mode of the data set. State which measure or measures of center best represent the data.

$$\{2.8, 1.2, 1.5, 2.0, 2.4, 1.8\}$$

SOLUTION

mean: $\dfrac{2.8 + 1.2 + 1.5 + 2.0 + 2.4 + 1.8}{6} = \dfrac{11.7}{6} = 1.95$

median: 1.2, 1.5, (1.8, 2.0) 2.4, 2.8; $\dfrac{1.8 + 2.0}{2} = 1.9$

Each value appears once. There is no mode.

The best measures of center are the mean and the median. ∎

Application: Management

EXAMPLE 5

A manager is writing a report describing the salaries of the workers at the store. The salaries are listed.

$$\{\,\$20{,}000;\ \$35{,}000;\ \$28{,}000;\ \$180{,}000;\ \$20{,}000\,\}$$

Find the mean, median, and mode of the data. Which measure or measures best represent the data? Explain your reasoning.

SOLUTION

The mean is $\dfrac{\$283{,}000}{5} = \$56{,}600$

The data in order are $20,000; $20,000; $28,000; $35,000; $180,000.

The median is $28,000.

The mode is $20,000.

The measure that best represents the data is the median. The mean is not a good measure because the outlier of $180,000 makes the mean a much greater number than the median. The mode is not a good measure because it is also the minimum value of the set. ∎

Measures of Variability

Measures of variability show the spread in a set of data.

Definitions

An **absolute deviation** is the absolute value of the difference between a data value and the mean. The **mean absolute deviation**, or MAD, is the mean of all the absolute deviations.

▶ **Think About It** There are other measures of variability besides the mean absolute deviation, but they often involve more complex calculations than the MAD.

To find the MAD of a set of data, first calculate the absolute deviation of each data value in the data set. Then add all the absolute deviations and divide by the number of data values.

EXAMPLE 1

Find the mean absolute deviation of the data.

A $\{6, 8, 11, 13, 17\}$

SOLUTION
Find the mean of the data.

$$\frac{6 + 8 + 11 + 13 + 17}{5} = \frac{55}{5} = 11$$

Calculate the absolute deviation for each data value and add.

$$|6-11| + |8-11| + |11-11| + |13-11| + |17-11|$$
$$= |-5| + |-3| + |0| + |2| + |6|$$
$$= 5 + 3 + 0 + 2 + 6$$
$$= 16$$

Divide the sum by the number of data values.

$$\frac{16}{5} = 3.2$$

The mean absolute deviation of the data set is 3.2.

B $\{3.1, 14.6, 19.7, 31.5, 37.8, 43.2\}$

▶ **Think About It** For large data sets, you should use a calculator to find the mean absolute deviation.

SOLUTION

Find the mean of the data.

$$\frac{3.1 + 14.6 + 19.7 + 31.5 + 37.8 + 43.2}{6} = \frac{149.9}{6} = 24.9833 \ldots \approx 25$$

Calculate the absolute deviation for each data value and add.

$$|3.1-25| + |14.6-25| + |19.7-25| + |31.5-25| + |37.8-25| + |43.2-25|$$
$$= |-21.9| + |-10.4| + |-5.3| + |6.5| + |12.8| + |18.2|$$
$$= 21.9 + 10.4 + 5.3 + 6.5 + 12.8 + 18.2$$
$$= 75.1$$

Divide the sum by the number of data values.

$$\frac{75.1}{6} = 12.51666 \ldots \approx 12.5$$

The mean absolute deviation of the data set is about 12.5. ∎

Application: Quiz Scores

EXAMPLE 2

A teacher divided a group of 16 students into two groups of 8 students each. She recorded each student's score on a quiz.

Group 1 87, 88, 96, 91, 78, 90, 83, 95

Group 2 95, 80, 87, 76, 89, 91, 82, 96

> ▶ **Think About It** A data set is not always ordered from least to greatest. However, the mean absolute deviation is the same whether the data are ordered or unordered.

A Calculate the MAD of each group's quiz scores.

SOLUTION

Group 1 Calculate the mean of the quiz scores.

$$\frac{87 + 88 + 96 + 91 + 78 + 90 + 83 + 95}{8} = \frac{708}{8} = 88.5$$

Add the absolute deviations and divide the sum by the number of data items.

$$|87 - 88.5| + |88 - 88.5| + |96 - 88.5| + |91 - 88.5| + |78 - 88.5|$$
$$+ |90 - 88.5| + |83 - 88.5| + |95 - 88.5|$$
$$= |-1.5| + |-0.5| + |7.5| + |2.5| + |-10.5| + |1.5| + |-5.5| + |6.5|$$
$$= 1.5 + 0.5 + 7.5 + 2.5 + 10.5 + 1.5 + 5.5 + 6.5 = 36$$

Divide the sum by 8 to get the MAD.

$$\frac{36}{8} = 4.5$$

Group 2 Calculate the mean of the quiz scores.

$$\frac{95 + 80 + 87 + 76 + 89 + 91 + 82 + 96}{8} = \frac{696}{8} = 87$$

Add the absolute deviations and divide the sum by the number of data items.

$$|95 - 87| + |80 - 87| + |87 - 87| + |76 - 87| + |89 - 87| + |91 - 87|$$
$$+ |82 - 87| + |96 - 87|$$
$$= |8| + |-7| + |0| + |-11| + |2| + |4| + |-5| + |9|$$
$$= 8 + 7 + 0 + 11 + 2 + 4 + 5 + 9 = 46$$

Divide the sum by 8 to get the MAD.

$$\frac{46}{8} = 5.75$$

The MAD of Group 1's quiz scores is 4.5. The MAD of Group 2's quiz scores is 5.75.

B Which group has the larger variation in their quiz scores? Explain your reasoning.

SOLUTION

Group 2 has the larger variation in their quiz scores. The MAD is a measure of the variation, or spread, of a set of data. Because the MAD of Group 2's scores, 5.75, is larger than the MAD of Group 1's scores, 4.5, Group 2 has the larger variation in their quiz scores. ■

Application: Manufacturing

EXAMPLE 3

A hardware manufacturer selects 9 bolts from a batch of newly made bolts. The bolt widths are 5.7, 5.8, 5.8, 5.9, 6, 6, 6, 6, and 6.1 mm.

A Find the MAD of the bolt widths. Round to the nearest hundredth.

SOLUTION

Determine the mean bolt width.

$$\frac{5.7 + 5.8 + 5.8 + 5.9 + 6 + 6 + 6 + 6 + 6.1}{9} = \frac{53.3}{9} = 5.9222 \ldots \approx 5.9$$

Calculate the MAD.

$$|5.7 - 5.9| + |5.8 - 5.9| + |5.8 - 5.9| + |5.9 - 5.9| + |6 - 5.9|$$
$$+ |6 - 5.9| + |6 - 5.9| + |6 - 5.9| + |6.1 - 5.9|$$
$$= |-0.2| + |-0.1| + |-0.1| + |0| + |0.1| + |0.1| + |0.1| + |0.1| + |0.2|$$
$$= 0.2 + 0.1 + 0.1 + 0 + 0.1 + 0.1 + 0.1 + 0.1 + 0.2 = 1.0$$

Divide the sum by 9 to get the MAD.

$$\frac{1.0}{9} = 0.111 \ldots \approx 0.11$$

The MAD of the bolt widths is about 0.11 mm.

B Explain what the value of the MAD represents.

SOLUTION

The MAD is a measure of the variation in bolt widths about their mean value of 5.9 mm. The larger the MAD, the more variation there would be in the width of the bolts manufactured. ■

Samples and Prediction

You can use information about part of a group to make predictions about the entire group. The way you choose a part of a group affects how useful your prediction about the whole group will be.

If a population is small, you can survey, or question, the entire population. However, if a population is large, such as every citizen in a certain state, it is more practical to survey a sample of the population.

Definitions

A **population** is a group of individuals or objects that you want information about. A **sample** is part of the population.

Identifying Bias and Possible Sources of Bias

For a sample to be useful, it must be representative of the population. A representative sample generally has the same characteristics as the population. For example, if most of a population is female, then most of the sample should be female.

Definitions

An **unbiased sample** is representative of the population. A **biased sample** is not representative of the population.

EXAMPLE 1

State whether the sample is likely to be biased. Identify possible sources of bias.

A Claire wants to know if the people in her neighborhood think that the speed limit on their street should be reduced. She asks the parents of the children she babysits.

SOLUTION
It is unlikely that everyone in the neighborhood is a parent, so the sample is probably not representative of the population. Parents are likely to think of their children's safety and request lower speed limits. The sample is likely to be biased.

B A boss wants to know if his employees would be interested in a company picnic. He prints an alphabetical list of all the employee names and asks every 10th person on the list.

SOLUTION
This sample is likely to be representative of all the employees, so it is likely to be unbiased.

C A reporter wants to know how many people in a town are interested in rock climbing. She goes to a sporting-goods store and asks every 10th person who exits.

SOLUTION
People who shop in a sporting-goods store are more likely to be interested in sports, such as rock climbing. The sample is likely to be biased.

> ▶ **Think About It** Bias depends on the population you are working with. For instance, in Example 1C, if the reporter wanted to know how many patrons of that store are interested in rock climbing, this sampling method would not be bad.

D On a TV news program, viewers are asked to go to the program's website and tell whether they are opposed to a recent tax increase.

SOLUTION

People opposed to the tax increase are more likely to make the effort to record their opinions than people who are not opposed. Also, not all viewers will have access to the Internet. For these reasons, the sample is likely to be biased. ■

Making Predictions About a Population

A prediction is an educated guess, or estimate. It is important to keep in mind the following points when making a prediction about a population:

- Estimates tend to become more accurate as the size of the sample increases. For example, an estimate based on a sample of 100 is likely to be better than an estimate based on a sample of 50.

- An estimate based on an unbiased sample is likely to be better than an estimate based on a biased sample.

> ▶ **Remember** A biased sample does not represent the population well.

EXAMPLE 2

In a sample of 100 people at a stadium, 72 preferred Brand A mustard to Brand B mustard. Predict about how many of the estimated 62,000 people in the stadium would prefer Brand A mustard.

SOLUTION

Write and solve a proportion.

$$\frac{x}{62{,}000} = \frac{72}{100} \qquad \text{Write a proportion.}$$

$$100x = 4{,}464{,}000 \qquad \text{Cross multiply.}$$

$$x = 44{,}640 \qquad \text{Divide both sides by 100.}$$

Based on the sample, about 44,640 people in the stadium would prefer Brand A. ■

> ▶ **Think About It** In Example 2, you could simplify the fraction before cross multiplying.

EXAMPLE 3

A study showed that 14% of the plants randomly sampled in a field were damaged by pests. Predict how many of the 750 plants from that field will show damage by pests.

SOLUTION

Find 14% of 750.

$$14\% \text{ of } 750 = 14\% \cdot 750 \qquad \text{The word } of \text{ indicates multiplication.}$$

$$= 0.14 \cdot 750 \qquad \text{Write the percent as a decimal.}$$

$$= 105 \qquad \text{Multiply.}$$

Based on the study, about 105 plants will show damage by pests. ■

Drawing Inferences

You can draw inferences about a population from a random sample.

Drawing Inferences from a Single Sample

You can draw inferences from a single random sample of a population. Perform calculations on the sample data and then assume that the results of the calculation extend to the whole population. For example, to estimate the mean of a population, calculate the mean of the randomly sampled data.

▶ **Think About It** An **inference** is a conclusion reached from facts, evidence, and reasoning.

EXAMPLE 1

A survey was taken of Belleville's 6741 voters. Two hundred voters were selected at random and asked which candidate for mayor they preferred.

Candidate	Baker	Jimenez	Washington
Number of voters	33	59	108

A candidate with more than 50% of the vote will win the election for mayor. What can you infer about who will win the election?

▶ **Remember** Estimates tend to become more accurate as the size of the sample increases.

SOLUTION

In the survey, voters preferred Washington (108 voters out of 200 surveyed). The percent equivalent of this ratio is

$$\frac{108}{200} \cdot 100\% = 0.54 \cdot 100\% = 54\%.$$

Because the survey was a random sample, its results represent the preference of the entire population of Belleville's voters. Therefore, you can infer that Washington will win with about 54% of the vote. ■

EXAMPLE 2

In a school population of 568 students, Janelle selected 20 students at random. She asked each of them how many pets he or she had at home. Janelle recorded the results in a table.

▶ **Remember** A frequency table shows the number of times a data value occurs.

Number of pets	Number of Students
0	5
1	7
2	4
3	2
4	1
5	1

▶ **Q&A**

Q What are the median and mode of the data set?

A median $= 1.5$, mode $= 1$

A Estimate the mean number of pets in the 568 students' homes.

SOLUTION

Calculate the mean using the sample data.

$$\frac{\overbrace{(0+\ldots+0)}^{5} + \overbrace{(1+\ldots+1)}^{7} + \overbrace{(2+\ldots+2)}^{4} + (3+3) + 4 + 5}{20}$$

$$= \frac{5(0) + 7(1) + 4(2) + 6 + 4 + 5}{20}$$

$$= \frac{0 + 7 + 8 + 6 + 4 + 5}{20} = \frac{30}{20} = 1.5$$

The estimated mean number of pets in students' homes is 1.5.

B Estimate the mean absolute deviation in the number of pets in the 568 students' homes.

SOLUTION

Calculate the mean absolute deviation using the sample data.

$$\frac{5|0 - 1.5| + 7|1 - 1.5| + 4|2 - 1.5| + 2|3 - 1.5| + |4 - 1.5| + |5 - 1.5|}{20}$$

$$= \frac{5|-1.5| + 7|-0.5| + 4|0.5| + 2|1.5| + |2.5| + |3.5|}{20}$$

$$= \frac{5(1.5) + 7(0.5) + 4(0.5) + 2(1.5) + 2.5 + 3.5}{20}$$

$$= \frac{7.5 + 3.5 + 2 + 3 + 2.5 + 3.5}{20} = \frac{22}{20} = 1.1$$

The estimated mean absolute deviation of pets in students' homes is 1.1. ■

Drawing Inferences from Multiple Samples

You can draw multiple random samples from a population to check whether the sample selection process is biased. The samples whose results agree are more likely to be representative of the population. The sample whose results differ from the other samples is likely to be biased and thus not representative of the population.

> ▶ **Remember** A sample is biased if some items or individuals in a population are favored over others.

EXAMPLE 3

A restaurant took four separate samples of its customers to find out which kind of salad they preferred. In each sample, 50 customers were selected at random and their salad preference recorded.

Sample	Caesar	fruit	house
1	14	14	22
2	26	18	6
3	13	16	21
4	16	14	20

> ▶ **Think About It** Businesses often conduct surveys of their customers to better understand their customers' favorite products and services.

A According to each sample, what can the restaurant infer about which salad customers prefer?

SOLUTION

According to Samples 1, 3, and 4, the restaurant can infer that its customers prefer the house salad over either the Caesar salad or the fruit salad. However, according to Sample 2, the customers seem to prefer the Caesar salad over either the fruit salad or the house salad.

B What could explain why the results from Sample 2 differ from the other samples? What could the restaurant do to handle this discrepancy?

SOLUTION

The sampling process used to collect Sample 2 could be different from the sampling process used to collect Samples 1, 3, and 4. Sample 2 could be biased due to a poor sampling technique.

Because the results from Samples 1, 3, and 4 agree, the restaurant could infer that those results represent customers' salad preference. The restaurant could also infer that the results from Sample 2 are not representative, so Sample 2 could be ignored. ■

Comparing Distributions

You can describe the overlap between two data sets numerically and based on shape.

Using Distributions to Determine Data Set Overlap

Definition

The **distribution** of a data set is the shape of the plotted data over the range of the data set's values.

Similar Distributions

Two data sets' distributions are similar if both their central values are approximately equal and their spreads are approximately equal.

You can compare two data sets by

- Inspecting the shape of their distributions, looking for the amount they overlap.

- Calculating the difference in their means and comparing this difference to the mean absolute deviation.

EXAMPLE 1

Two teams of 12 people each played golf. Each team's scores were recorded and displayed in a line plot.

> **Think About It** To compare the overlap of two distributions best, line the plots up vertically so that their labels match.

Team 1

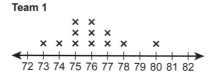

Team 2

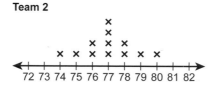

A Estimate the center of each data set based on shape.

SOLUTION

The center of Team 1's score distribution is about 76. The center of Team 2's score distribution is about 77.

B Describe the degree of overlap of the two data sets in terms of their centers and variability.

SOLUTION

Both teams have about the same mean score, around 76 to 77. The spread of the data is about the same for both data sets. The degree of overlap of the two data sets is high. ■

EXAMPLE 2

After a hailstorm, a meteorologist recorded the diameters, in millimeters, of hailstones at two different sites.

Site 1 $\{4, 6, 7, 5, 7, 5, 5, 6, 6, 9\}$

Site 2 $\{8, 11, 9, 10, 14, 8, 11, 10, 9, 10\}$

A Create a line plot for each data set. Estimate the center of each data set based on shape.

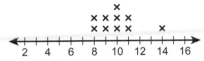

▶ **Q&A**

Q What is the median of each distribution?

A Site 1: median $= 6$
Site 2: median $= 10$

SOLUTION

The center of Site 1's score distribution is about 6 mm. The center of Site 2's score distribution is about 10 mm.

B Calculate the mean and MAD of each data set.

SOLUTION

Site 1

mean: $\dfrac{4 + 3(5) + 3(6) + 2(7) + 9}{10}$

$= \dfrac{4 + 15 + 18 + 14 + 9}{10} = \dfrac{60}{10} = 6$

MAD: $\dfrac{|4 - 6| + 3|5 - 6| + 3|6 - 6| + 2|7 - 6| + |9 - 6|}{10}$

$= \dfrac{|-2| + 3|-1| + 3|0| + 2|1| + |3|}{10} = \dfrac{10}{10} = 1$

The mean diameter is 6 mm, and the mean absolute deviation is 1 mm.

Site 2

mean: $\dfrac{2(8) + 2(9) + 3(10) + 2(11) + 14}{10}$

$= \dfrac{16 + 18 + 30 + 22 + 14}{10} = \dfrac{100}{10} = 10$

MAD: $\dfrac{2|8 - 10| + 2|9 - 10| + 3|10 - 10| + 2|11 - 10| + |14 - 10|}{10}$

$= \dfrac{2|-2| + 2|-1| + 3|0| + 2|1| + |4|}{10} = \dfrac{12}{10} = 1.2$

The mean diameter is 10 mm, and the mean absolute deviation is 1.2 mm.

C Compare the estimated mean and the MAD of the two data sets. What does this comparison say about the degree of overlap of the two data sets' distributions?

SOLUTION

The difference in the two means is $10 - 6 = 4$. This difference is much larger than the spread of hailstone diameters at either site, at least 3 times larger than either of the MAD values. The degree of overlap between the two distributions is low. ∎

Using Statistical Measures

You can determine whether two distributions are similar by comparing their means numerically.

Comparing Two Distributions

Means-to-MAD Ratio

$$\text{means-to-MAD ratio} = \frac{|\overline{X}_1 - \overline{X}_2|}{\text{MAD}_{\text{larger}}}$$

You can use the means-to-MAD ratio to describe the similarity of two distributions. Divide the positive difference in the means by the larger of the two MAD values. If this ratio is 1 or less, the two distributions are similar. If this ratio is between 1 and 2.5, the two distributions are somewhat similar. If this ratio is greater than 2.5, the two distributions are different.

EXAMPLE 1

Kim and Lisa had a friendly competition to determine who is better at a card game. They played 10 games of cards and recorded their scores. The person with the highest score won each round.

Game	1	2	3	4	5	6	7	8	9	10
Kim	−2	0	2	−1	0	3	0	1	8	−1
Lisa	−2	7	−1	2	0	1	3	−1	0	1

Think About It When creating a line plot, put the data in order first, and then plot the data. Check the correctness of your plot by comparing the ordered data values against the plot.

A Create a line plot for each data set.

SOLUTION

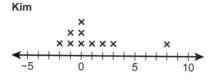

B Find the mean and MAD of each data set.

SOLUTION

Kim

mean: $\dfrac{(-2) + 2(-1) + 3(0) + 1 + 2 + 3 + 8}{10} = \dfrac{10}{10} = 1$

MAD: $\dfrac{|-2 - 1| + 2|-1 - 1| + 3|0 - 1| + |1 - 1| + |2 - 1| + |3 - 1| + |8 - 1|}{10}$

$= \dfrac{|-3| + 2|-2| + 3|-1| + |0| + |1| + |2| + |7|}{10} = \dfrac{20}{10} = 2$

Kim's mean score is 1, with a MAD of 2.

Lisa

mean: $\dfrac{(-2) + 2(-1) + 2(0) + 2(1) + 2 + 3 + 7}{10} = \dfrac{10}{10} = 1$

MAD: $\dfrac{|-2 - 1| + 2|-1 - 1| + 2|0 - 1| + 2|1 - 1| + |2 - 1| + |3 - 1| + |7 - 1|}{10}$

$= \dfrac{|-3| + 2|-2| + 2|-1| + 2|0| + |1| + |2| + |6|}{10} = \dfrac{18}{10} = 1.8$

Lisa's mean score is 1, with a MAD of 1.8.

c Can you infer that one player is better than the other? Why or why not?

SOLUTION

The difference in the two data sets' means is $1 - 1 = 0$. The difference in their mean scores is less than 1. With a means-to-MAD ratio of $\dfrac{0}{2} = 0$, you can conclude that both data sets have similar distributions. Therefore, you cannot infer that Kim or Lisa is the better player. ■

Comparing Two Populations from Samples

In some situations, it is not easy or even possible to collect data on every member in a population. Instead, you can compare two populations by obtaining samples from the populations and calculating the means-to-MAD ratio from the sample data.

▶ **Remember** The larger the sample size, the better the sample represents the entire population.

EXAMPLE 2

An orchard has two types of red apples. The orchard owner wants to know which variety of red apple produces bigger fruit. The farmer selects 9 apples at random from each variety and measures the circumference, in centimeters, of each apple.

Variety A $\{24, 26, 24, 25, 23, 23, 25, 24, 22\}$

Variety B $\{26, 27, 28, 30, 24, 26, 27, 27, 28\}$

A Create a line plot for each data set.

SOLUTION

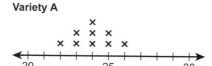

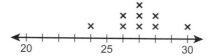

B Find the mean and MAD of each data set.

▶ **Think About It** To calculate the mean and MAD of a large data set, you can use computer software such as a spreadsheet or database program.

SOLUTION
Variety A

mean: $\dfrac{22 + 2(23) + 3(24) + 2(25) + 26}{9} = \dfrac{216}{9} = 24$

MAD: $\dfrac{|22 - 24| + 2|23 - 24| + 3|24 - 24| + 2|25 - 24| + |26 - 24|}{9}$

$= \dfrac{|-2| + 2|-1| + 3|0| + 2|1| + |2|}{9} = \dfrac{8}{9} \approx 0.9$

Variety A's mean circumference is 24 cm, with a MAD of 0.9 cm.

Variety B

mean: $\dfrac{24 + 2(26) + 3(27) + 2(28) + 30}{9} = \dfrac{243}{9} = 27$

MAD: $\dfrac{|24 - 27| + 2|26 - 27| + 3|27 - 27| + 2|28 - 27| + |30 - 27|}{9}$

$= \dfrac{|-3| + 2|-1| + 3|0| + 2|1| + |3|}{9} = \dfrac{10}{9} \approx 1.1$

Variety B's mean circumference is 27 cm, with a MAD of 1.1 cm.

C Can you infer that one variety of apples is larger than the other? Why or why not?

SOLUTION

Variety A's mean circumference is 24 cm, and Variety B's mean circumference is 27 cm, 3 cm larger. The positive difference in the means is $27 - 24 = 3$. With a means-to-MAD ratio of $\dfrac{3}{1.1} \approx 3$, you can conclude that their distributions are different. You can infer that Variety B apples are larger than Variety A apples. ■

Probability

What is the chance of hitting a bull's-eye? What about the chance of hitting a certain region of the target three times in a row? The tools of probability can help you make sense of situations that have an element of luck or chance.

Calculating Probability

Probability is a measure of how likely it is that something will happen.

In the study of probability, some terms have different meanings from what you might be used to. For instance, you might think that an experiment is something that scientists do, an event is some sort of social gathering, and a trial involves a judge.

Understanding Basic Concepts of Probability

Definitions	
Statement	**Example**
An **experiment** is any process or action that has a result.	Roll a 6-sided number cube.
A result is called an **outcome**.	A possible outcome is 4.
The set of all possible outcomes of an experiment is the **sample space**.	$\{1, 2, 3, 4, 5, 6\}$
An **event** is a set of one or more outcomes. An event is a subset of the sample space. Events are sometimes described as actions.	Roll a 4. $\{4\}$ Roll an even number. $\{2, 4, 6\}$ Roll a number less than 3. $\{1, 2\}$

If an experiment is performed more than once, each performance can be called a **trial**. For example, 100 rolls of a number cube can be described as 100 trials of an experiment.

Calculating Probability

▶ **Think About It** Unless otherwise noted, *probability* means theoretical probability. You will learn about experimental probability later in this chapter.

Probability of an Event (Theoretical Probability)

The **probability** of an event E, written $P(E)$, is a number from 0 to 1 that describes how likely event E is to occur. If all outcomes in the sample space S are equally likely, then

$$P(E) = \frac{\text{number of outcomes in event } E}{\text{total number of outcomes in sample space } S} = \frac{n(E)}{n(S)}.$$

You can write a probability as a fraction, decimal, or percent.

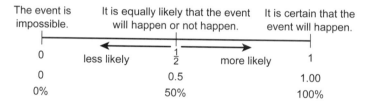

| The event is impossible. | It is equally likely that the event will happen or not happen. | It is certain that the event will happen. |

0   *less likely* $\frac{1}{2}$ *more likely*   1

0   0.5   1.00

0%   50%   100%

EXAMPLE 1

A 6-sided number cube is rolled.

A Find $n(S)$.

SOLUTION

The sample space S is $\{1, 2, 3, 4, 5, 6\}$, so there are 6 outcomes.

$$n(S) = 6$$

B Find $P(4)$.

SOLUTION

$P(4)$ represents the probability of rolling a 4. There is only 1 outcome that is a 4, so $n(4) = 1$.

$$P(4) = \frac{n(4)}{n(S)} = \frac{1}{6} \approx 0.17, \text{ or about } 17\%$$

C Find P(odd number).

SOLUTION

The event "roll an odd number" contains 3 outcomes: 1, 3, and 5.

$$P(\text{odd number}) = \frac{n(\text{odd number})}{n(S)} = \frac{3}{6} = \frac{1}{2} = 0.5 = 50\% \blacksquare$$

EXAMPLE 2

The integers 1 through 10 are written on 10 index cards, with a different integer on each card. The cards are placed in a bag. One card is chosen without looking.

A Find $n(S)$.

SOLUTION

There are 10 cards, so $n(S) = 10$.

B Find $P(\text{integer} > 7)$.

SOLUTION

$P(\text{integer} > 7)$ represents the probability of choosing an integer greater than 7. There are 3 outcomes in this event: 8, 9, and 10. So $n(\text{integer} > 7) = 3$.

$$P(\text{integer} > 7) = \frac{n(\text{integer} > 7)}{n(S)} = \frac{3}{10} = 0.3 = 30\%$$

C Find $P(12)$.

SOLUTION

There is no card with 12 written on it, so $n(12) = 0$.

$$P(12) = \frac{n(12)}{n(S)} = \frac{0}{10} = 0 = 0\%$$

D Find $P(\text{integer} < 12)$.

SOLUTION

Every integer in the bag is less than 12, so choosing an integer less than 12 is certain to happen.

$$P(\text{integer} < 12) = 1 = 100\% \quad \blacksquare$$

Calculating Probability Involving Complementary Events

If one of two events must occur, but both cannot occur at the same time, then those events are **complementary**. When two events are complementary, the sum of their probabilities is 1.

EXAMPLE 3

A bag contains 3 green marbles, 7 white marbles, and 5 red marbles (and no other marbles). One marble is chosen without looking.

▶ **Think About It** The definition of *probability* requires that all outcomes in the sample space are equally likely, so think of each marble as an outcome, not each color.

A Find $n(S)$.

SOLUTION

Since $3 + 7 + 5 = 15$, there are 15 outcomes in the sample space.

$$n(S) = 15$$

B Find $P(\text{green})$.

SOLUTION

$P(\text{green})$ represents the probability of choosing a green marble. There are 3 outcomes in this event, so $n(\text{green}) = 3$.

$$P(\text{green}) = \frac{n(\text{green})}{n(S)} = \frac{3}{15} = \frac{1}{5} = 0.2 = 20\%$$

C Find $P(\text{not green})$.

SOLUTION

Method 1 The outcomes that are *not green* are the outcomes *white* and *red*, so $n(\text{not green}) = n(\text{white}) + n(\text{red}) = 7 + 5 = 12$.

$$P(\text{not green}) = \frac{n(\text{not green})}{n(S)} = \frac{n(\text{white}) + n(\text{red})}{n(S)} = \frac{12}{15} = \frac{4}{5} = 0.8 = 80\%$$

Method 2 The outcomes *green* and *not green* are complementary because one of them must occur, but both cannot occur at the same time.

$$P(\text{green}) + P(\text{not green}) = 1$$
$$\frac{1}{5} + P(\text{not green}) = 1$$
$$P(\text{not green}) = 1 - \frac{1}{5} = \frac{4}{5} = 0.8 = 80\% \quad \blacksquare$$

Application: Weather

EXAMPLE 4

A meteorologist forecasts that the probability of snow is 70%. What is the probability that it will not snow?

SOLUTION

The outcomes *snow* and *no snow* are complementary, so $P(\text{snow}) + P(\text{no snow}) = 100\%$.

$$100\% - 70\% = 30\%$$

The probability that it will not snow is 30%. $\quad \blacksquare$

Relative Frequency

Increasing the number of trials improves the accuracy of the experiment.

Calculating Relative Frequency

Theoretical probability is based on the assumption that all outcomes in a sample space are equally likely. Relative frequency is based on actual observations or results of an experiment.

Relative Frequency of an Event (Experimental Probability)

If n is the number of trials of an experiment or number of observations in a study, then the relative frequency of an event E is

$$P(E) = \frac{\text{number of times event } E \text{ has occurred}}{n}.$$

▶ **Think About It** Experimental **probability** is another term for relative frequency.

EXAMPLE 1

Alicia rolls a number cube 50 times. The results are shown.

Outcome	1	2	3	4	5	6
Frequency	10	8	12	8	7	5

Based on the results, what is the relative frequency that the next roll will be a 3?

SOLUTION

The outcome 3 has occurred 12 times in 50 trials. Based on the results in the table, $P(3) = \dfrac{12}{50} = \dfrac{6}{25} = 0.24 = 24\%.$ ■

▶ **Think About It** Relative frequency might not equal theoretical probability. The theoretical probability of rolling a 3 is $\dfrac{1}{6}$, or about 17%.

EXAMPLE 2

Ramon chooses a marble from a bag without looking and then replaces it. He does this 75 times. The results are shown.

Outcome	red	white	blue
Frequency	7	40	28

Based on the results, what is the relative frequency of choosing a red marble?

▶ **Think About It** There is no way to calculate theoretical probability for the experiment in Example 2 because the contents of the bag are unknown.

SOLUTION

The outcome *red* has occurred 7 times out of 75 trials. Based on the results in the table, $P(\text{red}) = \dfrac{7}{75} \approx 0.093$, which is 9.3%. ■

Application: Surveys

EXAMPLE 3

A survey shows that 171 out of 460 students play a team sport. Based on the survey, what is the relative frequency that a student chosen at random plays a team sport?

SOLUTION

Based on the survey, the relative frequency that a student chosen at random plays a team sport is $\frac{171}{460}$, or about 0.372, which is 37.2%. ▪

Relative Frequency and Theoretical Probability

Law of Large Numbers

The **law of large numbers** states that the relative frequency of an event becomes closer to the theoretical probability of the event as the number of trials increases.

▶ **Think About It** The law of large numbers is another way of saying that increasing the sample size of a survey increases the survey's accuracy.

EXAMPLE 4

A coin was tossed 10 times, 100 times, and then 1000 times. The number of heads was recorded in a frequency table.

Number of tosses	10	100	1000
Heads	6	44	483

A Calculate the relative frequency of tossing heads for each sample size. Organize the results in a table.

SOLUTION

Number of tosses	10	100	1000
Relative frequency of heads	$\frac{6}{10} = 0.6 = 60\%$	$\frac{44}{100} = 0.44 = 44\%$	$\frac{483}{1000} = 0.483 = 48.3\%$

B The coin is a fair coin. What is the theoretical probability $P(\text{heads})$?

SOLUTION
The sample space S is $\{\text{heads, tails}\}$, so there are two equally probable outcomes.

$$P(\text{heads}) = \frac{1}{2} = 0.5 = 50\%$$

C Based on the theoretical probability, predict how many of 1000 coin flips will be heads.

SOLUTION
Multiply $P(\text{heads})$ by n, the number of coin flips.

$$P(\text{heads}) \cdot n = 0.50 \cdot 1000 = 500$$

Out of 1000 coin flips, is it expected that 500 will be heads.

D As the number n of trials increases from 10 to 1000, how does the value of the relative frequency change? Is this result expected?

SOLUTION
As n increases from 10 to 1000, the relative frequency gets closer to 50%. This result is expected according to the law of large numbers, which states that the relative frequency of an event becomes closer to its theoretical probability as the number of trials increases. ■

EXAMPLE 5

Jalisa has a bag that contains 10 marbles: some green, some red, and some blue. Jalisa randomly chooses a marble out of the bag, records the color, and then places that marble back in the bag. She repeats this experiment 3 times, increasing the number of trials from 10 to 50 and then to 200.

Outcome	10 Trials	50 Trials	200 Trials
green	6	28	104
red	2	18	78
blue	2	4	18

A Calculate the relative frequencies for each sample size and organize the results in a table.

SOLUTION

Outcome	10 Trials	50 Trials	200 Trials
green	$\frac{6}{10} = 0.6 = 60\%$	$\frac{28}{50} = 0.56 = 56\%$	$\frac{104}{200} = 0.52 = 52\%$
red	$\frac{2}{10} = 0.2 = 20\%$	$\frac{18}{50} = 0.36 = 36\%$	$\frac{78}{200} = 0.39 = 39\%$
blue	$\frac{2}{10} = 0.2 = 20\%$	$\frac{4}{50} = 0.08 = 8\%$	$\frac{18}{200} = 0.09 = 9\%$

B Can Jalisa calculate the theoretical probability that a green marble will be chosen? Why or why not?

SOLUTION

Jalisa does not know how many of each marble—green, red, or blue—is actually in the bag, so she cannot calculate the theoretical probability that a green marble will be chosen.

C Predict how many green, red, and blue marbles are actually in the bag. Explain your thinking.

SOLUTION

According to the law of large numbers, the relative frequency of an event is close to the theoretical probability of the event for a large number of trials.

For each marble type, multiply the relative frequency after 200 trials by 10, the actual number of marbles in the jar. Then round the product to the nearest whole number.

$$\text{green: } 10 \cdot 52\% = 10 \cdot 0.52 = 5.2 \approx 5$$
$$\text{red: } 10 \cdot 39\% = 10 \cdot 0.39 = 3.9 \approx 4$$
$$\text{blue: } 10 \cdot 9\% = 10 \cdot 0.09 = 0.9 \approx 1$$

It is likely that there are 5 green marbles, 4 red marbles, and 1 blue marble in the bag. ▪

▶ **Think About It** When rounding, check that the sum of the rounded numbers equals the total.

$$5 + 4 + 1 = 10$$

Probability Models

The theoretical probability of an event, calculated from a probability model, often differs from the event's relative frequency.

Application: Geometric Probability Model

Probability of an Event (Geometric Probability)

In a **geometric probability** model, the probability of an event (E) is

$$P(E) = \frac{\text{area of region of success}}{\text{area of entire region}}.$$

In a geometric probability model, a region representing successful outcomes is part of an entire region representing the sample space. Find the probability of an event by dividing the area of the region of success by the area of the entire region.

EXAMPLE 1

Nigel creates a circular dartboard. The radius of the dartboard is 10 in. At the center of the dartboard is a shaded circular region with a radius of 3 in. A player gets triple points if the dart lands in the shaded region.

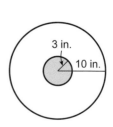

A Nigel throws a dart at the dartboard. Suppose the dart hits any spot on the dartboard at random. What is the probability that Nigel's throw earned triple points?

SOLUTION

In this situation,

$$\frac{\text{area of region of success}}{\text{area of entire region}} = \frac{\text{area of shaded region}}{\text{area of whole dartboard}}.$$

The shaded region and the whole dartboard are circles, so use the formula for the area of a circle, $A = \pi r^2$, to calculate the areas.

$$\frac{\text{area of shaded region}}{\text{area of whole dartboard}} = \frac{\pi(3)^2}{\pi(10)^2} = \frac{\pi \cdot 9}{\pi \cdot 100} = 0.09 = 9\%$$

The probability that Nigel's throw earned triple points is 9%.

B Nigel lands 100 throws on the dartboard. He earns triple points 11 times. Nigel says that the probability that the 101st throw earns triple points is 11%. Is Nigel correct? Explain.

SOLUTION

Nigel is not correct. He did calculate the relative frequency of 11% correctly. Nigel should use the geometric model to calculate the probability. In this model, the theoretical probability of a throw landing in the shaded region is 9%. It does not depend upon the results from previous throws. ■

> ▶ **Remember** Variation between experimental results and probabilities from a model is to be expected.

Application: Uniform Probability Model

In a uniform probability model, all outcomes are equally likely. Examples of processes following a uniform probability model include flipping a fair coin, tossing an unbiased number cube, and selecting a student from a class at random.

EXAMPLE 2

Chad has a fair die that he uses for a game. The die has the shape of a triangular pyramid, with 4 faces numbered 1 to 4. Chad rolled 100 times and recorded the results in a table.

Value	1	2	3	4
Number of rolls	22	29	26	23

A With what relative frequency did Chad roll an odd number?

SOLUTION

The relative frequency was

$$\frac{\text{number of rolls with 1 or 3}}{\text{total number of rolls}} = \frac{22 + 26}{100} = \frac{48}{100} = 0.48 = 48\%.$$

Chad rolled an odd number 48% of the time.

▶ **Q&A**

Q What is the probability that Chad rolls a prime number?

A $\frac{29 + 26}{100} = \frac{55}{100} = 0.55 = 55\%$

B What is the theoretical probability of Chad rolling an odd number?

SOLUTION

The die is fair, thus each roll would be equally probable. There are 4 possible rolls, so the probability of rolling an odd number is

$$\frac{\text{number of rolls with 1 or 3}}{\text{total number of rolls}} = \frac{2}{4} = \frac{1}{2} = 0.50 = 50\%.$$

The probability of Chad rolling an odd number is 50%.

C Because the theoretical probability of rolling an odd number differs from relative frequency observed, Chad says the die cannot be fair. Is Chad right? Explain your thinking with an example.

SOLUTION

Chad is not right. Often, relative frequencies do not exactly match the theoretical probabilities calculated from a model. For example, when a fair coin is tossed 100 times, heads should come up, on average, 50 times. However, the actual number of heads flipped would likely be a number close to 50, not 50 every time. ■

Combined Probability

For events A and B, you can find $P(A \text{ or } B)$ and $P(A \text{ and } B)$.

Events of an experiment may share outcomes.

Determining Whether Events Are Mutually Exclusive

If events do not share outcomes, they are mutually exclusive.

Definition
Mutually exclusive events cannot happen at the same time.

▶ **Think About It** Complementary events are mutually exclusive events.

EXAMPLE 1

A number cube is rolled. Determine whether the events are mutually exclusive.

A roll an even number, roll a prime number

SOLUTION
You roll an even number and a prime number at the same time when you roll a 2.

▶ **Think About It** A Venn diagram can help when you are analyzing sets of events.

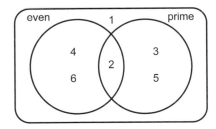

The events are not mutually exclusive.

B roll a 1, roll an even number

SOLUTION
You cannot roll a 1 and an even number at the same time.

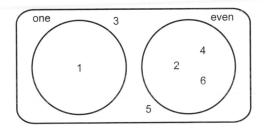

The events are mutually exclusive. ▪

Finding the Probability of Mutually Exclusive Events

Probability of Mutually Exclusive Events

For mutually exclusive events A and B,
$$P(A \text{ or } B) = P(A) + P(B).$$

EXAMPLE 2

The whole numbers from 1 to 20 are each written on a slip of paper and placed into a bag. A volunteer selects a slip of paper without looking.

A Find $P(3 \text{ or number} > 15)$.

SOLUTION

The events are mutually exclusive because you cannot select a 3 and a number greater than 15 at the same time.

$P(3 \text{ or number} > 15) = P(3) + P(\text{number} > 15)$

$$= \frac{1}{20} + \frac{5}{20}$$ There is 1 outcome in the first event $\{3\}$ and 5 outcomes in the second event $\{16, 17, 18, 19, \text{and } 20\}$.

$$= \frac{6}{20}$$

$$= \frac{3}{10}$$

B Find $P(\text{multiple of 7 or multiple of 10})$.

SOLUTION

The events are mutually exclusive because you cannot select a multiple of 7 and a multiple of 10 at the same time.

$P(\text{multiple of 7 or multiple of 10}) = P(\text{multiple of 7}) + P(\text{multiple of 10})$

$$= \frac{2}{20} + \frac{2}{20}$$ There are 2 outcomes in the first event $\{7, 14\}$ and 2 outcomes in the second event $\{10, 20\}$.

$$= \frac{4}{20}$$

$$= \frac{1}{5} \blacksquare$$

Determining Whether Events Are Independent or Dependent

Definitions

Two events are **independent events** if they are related in such a way that one event's occurrence has no effect on the probability of the other event.

Two events are **dependent events** if they are related in such a way that knowing about one event's occurrence has an effect on the probability of the other event.

EXAMPLE 3

Determine whether the events are independent or dependent.

A Select a red marble from a bag containing 10 red marbles and 10 yellow marbles, keep it out of the bag, and then select another red marble from the bag.

▶ **Think About It** When a situation involves selection without replacement, the sample space changes.

SOLUTION

For the first selection, $P(\text{red}) = \frac{10}{20} = \frac{1}{2}$ because there are 10 red marbles and 20 marbles in all. Knowing that a red marble was selected and not replaced changes $P(\text{red})$ to $\frac{9}{19}$ for the second selection, because there are only 9 red marbles and a total of 19 marbles left in the bag. The events are dependent.

B Select a red marble from a bag containing 10 red marbles and 10 yellow marbles, put it back in the bag, and then select a yellow marble from the bag.

SOLUTION

For the second selection, $P(\text{yellow}) = \frac{10}{20} = \frac{1}{2}$ because there are 10 yellow marbles and 20 marbles in all. Because the first marble is replaced before the second selection, the probability is $\frac{1}{2}$ regardless of which color is chosen first. The events are independent.

C Roll a 3 on a number cube 3 times in a row.

SOLUTION

$P(3)$ on each roll is $\frac{1}{6}$. The probabilities do not change for the second and third rolls because $n(E)$ and $n(S)$ remain 1 and 6, respectively. The events are independent. ▪

Finding the Probability of Independent Events

Probability of Independent Events

For independent events A and B,
$$P(A \text{ and } B) = P(A) \cdot P(B).$$

▶ **Think About It** The rule extends to three or more independent events.

EXAMPLE 4

Find the probability.

A A coin is tossed and a number cube is rolled. Find $P(\text{tails and even number})$.

SOLUTION

The events are independent because the probability of rolling an even number is not affected by the outcome of the coin toss.

$$P(\text{tails and even number}) = P(\text{tails}) \cdot P(\text{even number})$$
$$= \frac{1}{2} \cdot \frac{3}{6}$$
$$= \frac{3}{12}$$
$$= \frac{1}{4}$$

▶ **Think About It** There are 12 outcomes in the experiment of tossing a coin and rolling a number cube. Three of the outcomes contain both tails and an even number: $\{T2, T4, T6\}$.

B A bowl contains 3 pennies, 5 dimes, and 2 quarters. A coin is selected and replaced 3 times. Find $P(\text{penny then a penny then a quarter})$.

SOLUTION

The events are independent because each selection is replaced before the next selection.

$$P(\text{penny then a penny then a quarter}) = P(\text{penny}) \cdot P(\text{penny}) \cdot P(\text{quarter})$$
$$= \frac{3}{10} \cdot \frac{3}{10} \cdot \frac{2}{10}$$
$$= \frac{18}{1000}$$
$$= \frac{9}{500}$$ ■

Finding the Probability of Dependent Events

Probability of Dependent Events

For dependent events A and B,

$$P(A \text{ and } B) = P(A) \cdot P(B \text{ after } A)$$

where $P(B \text{ after } A)$ is the probability of B knowing that event A has already occurred.

▶ **Think About It** The rule extends to three or more dependent events.

EXAMPLE 5

A bag contains 8 white potatoes and 4 red potatoes. A cook selects a potato, puts it on the counter, and then selects another potato without looking.

A Find $P(\text{white and white})$.

SOLUTION
The probability of selecting a white potato on the second selection is different from selecting a white potato on the first selection because the sample space is different.

$P(\text{white and white}) = P(\text{white}) \cdot P(\text{white after white})$

$\qquad = \dfrac{8}{12} \cdot \dfrac{7}{11}$ 　　For the first selection, there are 8 white potatoes and 12 total potatoes. For the second selection, there are 7 white potatoes and 11 total potatoes.

$\qquad = \dfrac{56}{132}$

$\qquad = \dfrac{14}{33} \approx 42\%$

B Find $P(\text{white and red})$.

SOLUTION

$P(\text{white and red}) = P(\text{white}) \cdot P(\text{red after white})$

$\qquad\qquad\qquad\quad = \dfrac{8}{12} \cdot \dfrac{4}{11}$ For the second selection, there are 4 red potatoes and 11 total potatoes.

$\qquad\qquad\qquad\quad = \dfrac{32}{132}$

$\qquad\qquad\qquad\quad = \dfrac{8}{33} \approx 24\%$ ■

▶ **Think About It** For events involving selection without replacement, $n(S)$ will always change for the second probability. $n(F)$ may or may not change.

Compound Events

Compound events look at the probability of two or more events occurring at the same time.

Tree Diagrams, Lists, and Tables

Tree diagrams, organized lists, and two-way tables can help you find all the possible outcomes for a compound event and can be used to calculate the probability of any outcome.

Definition
Tree diagrams provide a visual representation of all the possible outcomes of an event. Each branch represents a possible outcome.

EXAMPLE 1

You are given a coin and a spinner. Determine all the possible outcomes of a coin toss and a spin of the spinner.

 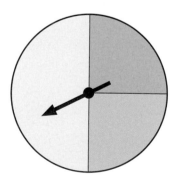

A Show and explain a tree diagram for all possible outcomes.

SOLUTION
Start the tree diagram by drawing branches for the 2 possible outcomes of the coin toss: heads or tails. From each outcome of the coin toss, draw branches for the 3 possible outcomes of spinning the spinner: blue, red, or yellow.

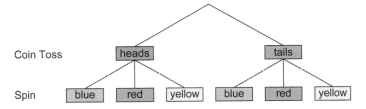

The tree diagram shows that there are 6 possible outcomes of a coin toss and a spin of the spinner: heads/blue, heads/red, heads/yellow, tails/blue, tails/red, and tails/yellow.

▶ **Think About It** You can choose to start the tree diagram with either the coin toss or the spinner. The total number of outcomes will be the same.

B Write an organized list of all of the possible outcomes shown in the tree diagram.

SOLUTION
Use a letter to represent each outcome, and then use the outcomes to write an organized list.

heads – H   blue – B
tails – T   red – R
             yellow – Y

The possible outcomes are HB, HR, HY, TB, TR, and TY.

C Draw a two-way table showing the possible outcomes.

SOLUTION

Label the columns with the outcomes of the coin toss and label the rows with the outcomes of a spin of the spinner.

	Heads	Tails
Blue	HB	TB
Red	HR	TR
Yellow	HY	TY

Finding Compound Probabilities

The probability of two independent events' occurring at the same time is the product of the probability of each individual event.

▶ **Remember** For independent events A and B,
$$P(A \text{ and } B) = P(A) \bullet P(B).$$

EXAMPLE 2

Determine the probabilities of possible outcomes from the coin toss and the spin of the spinner in Example 1.

A Find the probabilities of each outcome shown on the tree diagram in Example 1A.

SOLUTION

Step 1 Look at the probability of each event, the coin toss and the spin of the spinner, independently. The probability of getting heads or tails in the coin toss is $\frac{1}{2}$, or 50%, because there are only 2 possible outcomes.

The spinner has 4 equal sections: 1 blue, 1 red, and 2 yellow. The probability of the spinner's landing on blue is $\frac{1}{4}$, or 25%. The probability of the spinner's landing on red is $\frac{1}{4}$, or 25%. The probability of the spinner's landing on yellow is $\frac{2}{4}$, or 50%.

Step 2 Use the formula for the probability of independent events to find the probability for each outcome.

$P(\text{coin toss and spin}) = P(\text{coin toss}) \cdot P(\text{spin})$

$P(\text{heads and blue}) = P(\text{heads}) \cdot P(\text{blue})$ Choose 1 of the possible outcomes.

$$= \frac{1}{2} \cdot \frac{1}{4}$$

$$= \frac{1}{8}$$

The probability of the coin toss's landing on heads and the spinner's landing on blue is $\frac{1}{8}$, or 12.5%. Repeat these steps for all the other possible outcomes. The results are shown in the tree diagram.

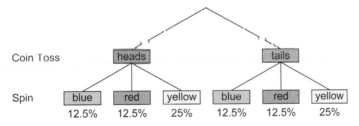

You can also write the probabilities in the two-way table.

	Heads	Tails
Blue	12.5%	12.5%
Red	12.5%	12.5%
Yellow	25%	25%

B Find the probability of the coin toss's landing on tails and the spinner's landing on blue or yellow.

SOLUTION

Step 1 Determine the probability of the spinner's landing on blue or yellow.

Add the probabilities of the spinner's landing on blue and the spinner's landing on yellow.

$$P(\text{blue or yellow}) = P(\text{blue}) + P(\text{yellow})$$
$$= \frac{1}{4} + \frac{1}{2}$$
$$= \frac{3}{4}$$

The probability of the spinner's landing on blue or yellow is $\frac{3}{4}$, or 75%.

Step 2 Calculate the probability of the coin toss's landing on tails and the spinner's landing on blue or yellow.

$$P(\text{tails and blue or yellow}) = P(\text{tails}) \cdot P(\text{blue or yellow})$$
$$= \frac{1}{2} \cdot \frac{3}{4}$$
$$= \frac{3}{8}$$

The probability of tails and a blue or yellow spin is $\frac{3}{8}$, or 37.5%. ∎

Pronunciation Guide

Pronunciation Guide

The tables provide sample words to explain the sounds associated with specific letters and letter combinations used in the respellings in this book. For example, *a* represents the short "a" sound in *cat*, while *ay* represents the long "a" sound in *day*.

Letter combinations are used to approximate certain more complex sounds. For example, in the respelling of *trapezoid*—TRA-puh-zoyd—the letters *uh* represent the vowel sound you hear in *shut* and *other*.

VOWELS

a	short a: **a**pple, c**a**t
ay	long a: c**a**ne, d**ay**
e, eh	short e: h**e**n, b**e**d
ee	long e: f**ee**d, t**ea**m
i, ih	short i: l**i**p, act**i**ve
iy	long i: tr**y**, m**i**ght
ah	short o: h**o**t, f**a**ther
oh	long o: h**o**me, thr**ow**
uh	short u: sh**u**t, **o**ther
yoo	long u: **u**nion, c**u**te

LETTER COMBINATIONS

ch	**ch**in, an**ci**ent
sh	**sh**ow, mi**ss**ion
zh	vi**s**ion, a**z**ure
th	**th**in, heal**th**
th	**th**en, hea**th**er
ur	b**ir**d, f**ur**ther, w**or**d
us	b**us**, cr**us**t
or	c**our**t, f**or**mal
ehr	**err**or, c**are**
oo	c**oo**l, tr**ue**, r**u**le
ow	n**ow**, **ou**t
ou	l**oo**k, p**u**ll, w**ou**ld
oy	c**oi**n, t**oy**
aw	s**aw**, m**au**l, f**a**ll
ng	so**ng**, fi**ng**er
air	**A**ristotle, b**a**rrister
ahr	c**ar**t, m**ar**tyr

CONSONANTS

b	**b**utter, **b**a**b**y
d	**d**og, cra**d**le
f	**f**un, **ph**one
g	**g**rade, an**g**le
h	**h**at, a**h**ead
j	**j**u**dg**e, **g**or**g**e
k	**k**ite, **c**ar, bla**ck**
l	**l**i**l**y, mi**l**e
m	**m**o**m**, ca**m**el
n	**n**ext, ca**n**did
p	**p**rice, co**pp**er
r	**r**ubbe**r**, f**r**ee
s	**s**mall, **c**ircle, ha**ss**le
t	**t**on, po**tt**ery
v	**v**ase, **v**i**v**id
w	**w**all, a**w**ay
y	**y**ellow, ka**y**ak
z	**z**ebra, ha**z**e

Glossary

abscissa   the first number in an ordered pair of numbers; also called the *x*-coordinate

absolute deviation   the absolute value of the difference between a data value and the mean

absolute value   the distance from zero to the graph of a number on a number line; The absolute value of a number *a* is denoted by $|a|$.

acute angle   an angle that measures greater than 0° and less than 90°

acute triangle   a triangle with three acute angles

addends   numbers that are added

addition pattern   a pattern formed by adding the same addend to each term to get the next term

additive identity   a number whose sum with any given number is the given number; The additive identity for the real numbers is zero.

additive inverses   two numbers whose sum, when added together, is zero; A number's additive inverse is its opposite.

adjacent angles   angles in the same plane that share a vertex and a side but do not share any interior points

algebraic expression   an expression containing variables as well as constant values

algorithm   a step-by-step way to solve a problem

alternate exterior angles   the outside angles that do not share the same vertex and are on opposite sides of a transversal crossing two lines

alternate interior angles   the inside angles that do not share the same vertex and are on opposite sides of a transversal crossing two lines

altitude   a line segment that extends from a figure's vertex and intersects the opposite side at a right angle

angle   a figure formed by two rays, called sides, that share the same endpoint

angle of rotation   the number of degrees a figure is rotated

apothem   a line segment that joins the center of a polygon to the midpoint of one of its sides

approximate solution   an estimate for the answer to a problem

area   the number of square units contained in the interior of a figure

arrangement   the order or placement of numbers or objects

average   the sum of the data divided by the number of data values; the mean of the data

axis   a number line that appears in a graph, such as the *x*-axis or *y*-axis in a coordinate plane; The plural of *axis* is *axes*.

bar graph   a graph that uses bars to display and compare data

base   a number or variable that is raised to a given power; For example, in 5^2, 5 is the base.

base of a cylinder   one of the parallel, congruent faces of the cylinder; A base of a cylinder is a circle.

base of a figure   the bottom side or face of a geometric figure

base of a parallelogram   the side of a parallelogram that is chosen as the bottom side; Any side of a parallelogram can be its base.

base of a prism   one of two parallel congruent faces in a prism

bias   the error that can arise when a sample is not representative of its population

biased sample   a sample that is not representative of its population

bisector   a line that divides a line segment, an angle, or another figure into two equal parts

boundary number   the upper or lower limit used to round a number to a given place value

box-and-whisker plot   a diagram that shows the distribution or spread of data with the minimum, the maximum, and the three quartiles of the data

capacity   a measure indicating an amount a container can hold

Cartesian coordinate system   method of locating points in a plane in which the coordinates of the points are their distances from two intersecting perpendicular lines called axes

categorical variable   a variable that has two or more categories

center of rotation   the point about which a figure is rotated

chord   a segment with endpoints that are points on a circle

circle   the set of all points in a plane that are equidistant from a given point called the center

circle graph   a circular chart that shows divisions according to how data results are distributed

circumference   distance around a circle

clockwise   in the same direction that the hands on a clock rotate

closed   a set is closed under an operation if the operation performed on any two numbers in the set produces another number in the set

cluster   a group of points that are close together in comparison to other points

coefficient   the numerical factor in a term in a variable term

coincident system of linear equations   consistent system of linear equations with infinitely many solutions; also called a consistent dependent system

collinear points   points that lie on the same line

combination   a collection of items in which the order of the items is not important

common factor   a factor that two or more given numbers have in common; For example, 9 and 12 have a common factor of 3.

compass   a tool used to draw circles and to measure in constructions

complementary angles   a pair of angles for which the sum of their measures is 90°

complementary events   two events such that one must occur, but both cannot occur at the same time

complex fraction   a fraction that has a fraction in the numerator or the denominator (or both)

composite number   a whole number greater than 1 that is not prime

compound interest   interest paid on both the principal (the original amount of money) and the interest an account has already earned

cone   a three-dimensional figure with one base that is a circle, a curved lateral surface, and a point called a vertex

congruent   having exactly the same size and shape, even though orientation may vary

congruent angles   angles that have the same measure

congruent figures   figures that have the same size and shape

congruent polygons   polygons that have the same size and shape

congruent triangles   triangles that are identical to each other

conjecture   an idea that might be true on the basis of observations but is not yet proven to be true

consecutive whole numbers   whole numbers that increase by 1, such as the numbers 3, 4, and 5

consistent dependent system of linear equations   a system of linear equations with infinitely many solutions; also called a coincident system

consistent independent system of linear equations a system of linear equations with exactly one solution

consistent system of linear equations a system having exactly one solution or infinitely many solutions

constant a numerical term that has no variables

constant function a function that neither rises nor falls as the input variable increases

constant of variation the ratio of two directly proportional quantities; also the nonzero constant k defined by $y = kx$ in a direct variation; also called the constant of proportionality

constant rate a rate that does not change over time

construction a method showing how a figure can be drawn accurately with a specified set of tools

continuous data values that all make sense within a range of data

contradiction an equation that is true for no values of the variable

convenience sampling sampling in which members of the population who are close at hand are selected

coordinate a number that indicates the location of a point on a number line

coordinate plane a plane that has an x-axis and a y-axis perpendicular to each other on which points can be located

corresponding angles angles that lie in the same position or match up with respect to the transversal when the transversal crosses two lines

counterclockwise in the opposite direction than the hands on a clock rotate

cross products the product of the numerator of one fraction and the denominator of a second fraction and the product of the denominator of the first fraction and the numerator of the second fraction

cross section a plane figure that results from the intersection of a plane and a solid

cube a solid figure made up of six square faces that meet at right angles

cubed the result of the operation where a number has been multiplied by itself two times, such as 5 cubed $= 5^3 = 5 \cdot 5 \cdot 5 = 125$; When the volume of a cube is found, the dimensions are cubed, and the volume is expressed in units cubed.

cube root a number that when multiplied by itself 3 times equals a given number

cubic unit a cube that is 1 unit on each side; a measure of volume

cylinder a three-dimensional figure with two congruent, parallel bases that are circles and a curved lateral surface that joins them

data numerical information that has been gathered; The term *data* is plural.

data skewed left the graph of the distribution of data with a longer tail to the left side

data skewed right the graph of the distribution of data with a longer tail to the right side

decimal a number written with a decimal point

decreasing function a function whose output values decrease as the input values increase

degree a unit used to measure angles

degree of accuracy the place value that is to be used to report an answer, such as in tens or hundredths

denominator the bottom number of a fraction

dependent events two events that are related in such a way that knowing about one event's occurrence has an effect on the probability of the other event

dependent variable the output variable

diameter a chord that passes through the center of a circle

diameter of a sphere a line segment passing through the center of a sphere that joins two points on the sphere

difference the solution to a subtraction problem

dilation   the change in size of a figure without a change in shape

direct linear variation   a function where y varies directly with x following the equation $y = kx$ where k is a nonzero constant

directly proportional   a relationship in which two quantities vary directly with each other

direct variation   a relationship between two quantities in which one quantity increases in proportion to the other; The relationship can be shown as a line on a graph.

discount   a decrease in the price of an item

discrete data   values that are distinct or have distinct intervals; values between the intervals that do not make sense as part of the data set

distribution of a data set   the shape of the plotted data over the range of the data set's values

distributive property   a rule that says that multiplying a number by a sum gives the same answer as multiplying the number by each addend of the sum and then adding the products

dividend   the number to be divided; The dividend divided by the divisor equals the quotient.

divide out a common factor   to simplify an expression by dividing a numerator and denominator by a common factor

divisor   the number that divides the dividend; The dividend divided by the divisor equals the quotient.

domain   the set of allowable inputs of a relation

equally likely   having the same chance of happening

equation   a number sentence that indicates that two expressions are equal

equiangular polygon   a polygon with all angles congruent

equiangular triangle   a triangle with three 60° angles

equilateral polygon   a polygon with all sides congruent

equilateral triangle   a triangle in which all three sides have equal length

equivalent   having the same value, such as $\frac{1}{2}$, 0.5, and 50%

equivalent equations   equations with the same solution or solutions

equivalent fractions   fractions with the same value

equivalent inequalities   inequalities that have the same solution set

equivalent ratios   ratios that describe the same numerical relationship

estimate (n.)   a very good guess or rough calculation of an answer, when the exact answer is not necessary

estimate (v.)   to make a very good guess or rough calculation of an answer when the exact answer is not necessary

evaluate   to find the value of an expression

evaluate a variable expression   to replace all the variables in the expression with numbers and simplify

event   a set of one or more outcomes; a subset of the sample space; also called actions

exact solution   a solution that is not an estimate or an approximation

experiment   any process or action that has a result

experimental probability   probability based on actual observations or results of an experiment

exponent   a number or variable attached to the base to show how many times the base will be a factor; For example, in 5^2, the exponent is 2.

expression   a group of mathematical symbols that represents a numerical value; Most expressions contain numerals as well as operation signs or grouping symbols or a combination of these elements. An expression containing one or more variables is a variable expression or an algebraic expression.

exterior angle of a triangle   an angle formed by two sides of a triangle, one of which extends outside the triangle; Each interior angle of a triangle forms a linear pair with an exterior angle.

extrapolation   the process of inferring, estimating, or predicting an unknown value that is outside of known values

extremes   in a proportion, the first and last numbers or variables; In $a : b = c : d$ or $\frac{a}{b} = \frac{c}{d}$, a and d are the extremes.

factor   any of two or more numbers multiplied to form a product

favorable outcome   the outcome you are investigating

flip   the movement of a figure that shows the figure and its mirror image, sometimes called a reflection

formula   an equation that is used to compute values, such as area, perimeter, or volume

fraction   a number that shows part of a set, a point on a number line, a part of a whole, a quotient, or a ratio

frequency   the number of times one item appears in a data set

frequency table   a table that shows how often each item appears in a set of data

friendly numbers   numbers such as 5 and 10, or multiples of 5 and 10, that are easier to add, subtract, multiply, and divide

function   a relation in which every element of the domain is assigned to exactly one element of the range

geometric probability   the probability of an event equal to the ratio of the area of success to the area of the entire region

graph (n.)   a diagram that shows the relationship between quantities

graph (v.)   to draw a visual representation of data

graph of a one-variable inequality   the set of points on a number line that represents all the solutions of the inequality

greatest common factor (GCF)   the greatest number that divides evenly into two or more numbers

grouping symbols   symbols such as parentheses, brackets, and fraction bars used to set apart an expression that should be simplified before other operations are performed

height   in a geometric figure, the length of an altitude that is perpendicular to a base

height of a triangle   the length of the perpendicular segment that joins a base to the opposite vertex

histogram   a graph with adjoining bars; used to show the frequency of data or data groups

horizontal intercept   the value of the variable on the horizontal axis at the point where a graph crosses the horizontal axis

hypotenuse   the side opposite the right angle in a right triangle

identity   an equation that is true for every value of the variable

image   the new figure that results from a transformation

improper fraction   a fraction in which the numerator is greater than or equal to the denominator

inconsistent system of linear equations   a system with no solution

increasing function   a function whose output values increase as input values increase

independent events   two events that are related in such a way that one event's occurrence has no effect on the probability of the other event

independent variable   the input variable

inequality   a mathematical sentence that compares numbers or expressions using one of the symbols $<, >, \leq,$ or $\geq$

inference   a conclusion reached from facts, evidence, and reasoning

input   a number that will be used in a rule to determine the value of the output

integers the set of whole numbers and their opposites $\{\dots -2, -1, 0, 1, 2, \dots\}$

intercept the value at which a graph crosses one of the coordinate axes

interest the cost to borrow money or the amount earned by lending money

interest rate the percentage of the original amount of money on which the interest will be calculated

interior angle any angle inside a polygon

interpolation the process of inferring, or estimating, an unknown value that is between known values

interquartile range (IQR) a measure of variation found by subtracting the first quartile Q_1 from the third quartile Q_3: $IQR = Q_3 - Q_1$; represents the range of the middle half of the data

intersecting lines lines that cross at one point

interval the distance between two points, as between two numbers on a number line

inverse operations opposite operations that undo each other; Subtraction and addition are inverse operations. Division and multiplication are inverse operations.

irrational number a real number that cannot be written in the form $\frac{a}{b}$ for integers a and b, with $b \neq 0$

irregular polygon a polygon that does not have all sides and angles equal in measure

isosceles triangle a triangle that has at least two sides equal in length; An equilateral triangle is a special type of isosceles triangle.

label one of the informative indicators at various places on data displays such as tables and graphs

lateral area the sum of the areas of a figure's lateral faces only

lateral face one of the parallelograms that form a prism and is not a base

lateral surface the curved surface of a cylinder or cone; in a prism, any surface that connects the two bases; in a pyramid, any surface that rises from the base to the vertex

lateral surface area the sum of the areas of all surfaces of a three-dimensional figure except the base(s)

law of large numbers a law that states that the relative frequency of an event becomes closer to the theoretical probability of the event as the number of trials increases

least common denominator (LCD) in a set of fractions, the least common multiple of the denominators

least common multiple (LCM) the least number that is a multiple of all numbers in a set

leg of a right triangle one of the two sides of a right triangle that form the right angle

like denominators denominators that are exactly the same in two or more fractions

like fractions fractions with the same denominator

like terms terms that have the same variable part(s) raised to the same powers; Constants (numbers without variables) are also like terms.

line a straight path of points that extends without end in both directions

linear association in a scatter plot, points following a pattern that resembles a line

linear equation an equation whose graph is a line

linear function a function whose graph is a straight line

linear pair two angles that have a common side and whose other sides point in opposite directions

line graph a display in which a set of information is shown as a series of points connected by straight line segments; A line graph is used to reveal trends.

line of reflection the line across which a figure is reflected

line plot a number line that shows all the data values with a mark or marks above each data value to show how many times that data value occurred

line segment part of a line including two points on the line and all the points between those points

literal equation   an equation with two or more variables; Formulas are common examples of literal equations.

lower bound estimate   an estimate for a problem that is less than the actual solution could be

lowest terms   when the numerator and the denominator of a fraction have no common factors other than 1

magic square   a square made up of an equal number of rows and columns of numbers such that the sum of any column, row, or diagonal is the same

maximum   the greatest value for a data set

mean absolute deviation (MAD)   the mean of all the absolute deviations of a data set

means   in a proportion, the second and third numbers or variables; In $a : b = c : d$ or $\frac{a}{b} = \frac{c}{d}$, b and c are the means.

mean   the sum of the values in a data set divided by the number of values

measure of center   a measure that represents the center of the distribution of values for a data set, such as mean, median, and mode

measure of spread   a measure that represents the extent to which the values of a data set are spread out, such as the range

measure of variation   a measure, such as the interquartile range, that compares the range or spread of data to a measure of center

median   the middle value when the data are ordered; If there is an even number of data values, the median is the average of the two middle values.

minimum   the least value for a data set

minuend   a number from which another number is subtracted

mixed number   a number consisting of both a whole number and a fraction, or the opposite of such a number

mode   the most common value; A data set can have no mode, one mode, or more than one mode.

multiple of a number   the product of the given number and a counting number

multiplication pattern   a pattern formed by multiplying each term by the same factor to get the next term

multiplicative identity   the number 1

multiplicative inverse   the reciprocal of a number

mutually exclusive events   events that cannot happen at the same time

negative association   in a scatter plot, a relationship between two variables for which an increase in one variable corresponds to a decrease in the other variable

negative correlation   a trend that develops with two variables when the value of one variable increases while the other value decreases; In a scatter plot, the data points form a pattern that slants down.

negative sign   the sign $(-)$ indicating that a number's value is less than zero, such as -6

net   a two-dimensional pattern that can be folded into a three-dimensional figure

net gain or net loss   the sum of the individual values when a situation includes several gains and losses

no association   in a scatter plot, a relationship between two variables for which an increase in one variable doesn't correspond to any particular pattern for the other variable

nonlinear association   in a scatter plot, points following a pattern that does not resemble a line

nonlinear function   a function whose graph is not a straight line

nonrepeating decimal   a nonterminating decimal that has no repeating pattern of digits

nonterminating decimal   a decimal that does not terminate or end

nonzero opposites   two numbers that are the same distance from zero on a number line

nth root any number x such that x raised to the n power equals some given number a for a whole number $n > 1$

number line a line that has equally spaced intervals labeled with coordinates

numerator the top number of a fraction

numerical expression an expression consisting of numbers and one or more operations

obtuse angle an angle that measures greater than $90°$ and less than $180°$

obtuse triangle a triangle with an obtuse angle

open sentence an equation or inequality that contains one or more variables

opposites a pair of numbers whose distance on both sides of zero is the same, such as -5 and $+5$

ordered pair a pair of numbers in which the first number is the x-coordinate, or abscissa, and the second number is the y-coordinate, or ordinate, of a point's location in the coordinate plane

order-of-magnitude estimate an estimate expressed as a power of 10

order of operations mathematical order that should be followed to simplify an expression when there is more than one operation

ordinate the second number in an ordered pair of numbers; the y-coordinate

origin on a number line, the point with coordinate zero; on a coordinate plane, the point where the x-axis and the y-axis intersect; The ordered pair at the origin is $(0, 0)$.

outcome a result of an experiment

outlier a point that is far from other points in a data set

output the result of applying a function rule to the value of an input

parallel lines lines on the same plane that never intersect

parallelogram a quadrilateral with two pairs of parallel sides

percent a ratio that compares a number to 100

percent error the ratio of the absolute error of a measurement to the actual value, written as a percent

percent of change the ratio of the amount of change to the original amount, expressed in percent form

perfect square a rational number with a rational square root

perimeter distance around a figure; The perimeter of a polygon is the sum of the lengths of all the sides.

perpendicular lines lines that intersect and form angles that measure $90°$

place value the value of a digit depending on its position, or place, in a number

plane a flat surface with infinite length and width but no thickness

point a location in space with no length, width, or depth

point on a coordinate plane a dot that marks a coordinate; a location on a coordinate plane, designated by an x-value and a y-value

point-slope form of a linear equation
$y - y_1 = m(x - x_1)$ where m is the slope of the line and x_1 and y_1 are the coordinates of a point through which the line passes

polygon a closed figure formed by three or more line segments in a plane, such that each line segment intersects two other line segments at their endpoints only

population a group of individuals or objects about which information is wanted

positive association in a scatter plot, a relationship between two variables for which an increase in one variable corresponds to an increase in the other variable

positive correlation a trend that describes when two variables increase or decrease together; In a scatter plot, the data points form a pattern that slants up.

positive sign the sign $(+)$ indicating that a number's value is greater than zero, such as $+6$; The positive sign is not always shown.

power the product that results when a number, called the base, is multiplied by itself the number of times indicated by its exponent

power of ten any number that can be written in the form $10n$, where n is an integer

precision an indication of how exact a calculation or measurement is

predict to state how future events will happen

pre-image the original figure in a transformation

prime factorization an expression showing a positive integer as a product of its prime factors

prime number a whole number greater than 1 that has only two whole-number factors, 1 and itself

principal money that earns interest at a given rate over time; The principal is the original amount of money on which the interest is based.

principal square root the nonnegative square root, indicated by the square root sign

prism a three-dimensional figure whose surfaces, called faces, are polygons; At least two faces are parallel and congruent and are called bases, and all other faces are parallelograms. (In a right prism, all other faces are rectangles.)

probability a number from 0 to 1 that describes how likely an event is to occur

product the result of multiplying two or more factors together

proper fraction a fraction in which the numerator is less than the denominator

proportion an equation stating that two ratios are equal

proportional relationship a relationship that can be described by an equation of the form $y = kx$ where k is the constant of proportionality

protractor a tool to measure the degrees in an angle

pyramid a three-dimensional figure with one base that is a polygon and all other faces (called lateral faces) are triangles that meet at a single vertex

quadrant one of the four regions into which the coordinate axes separate the coordinate plane

quadratic variation a relationship between x and y in which you can write the function describing the relationship in a form of the general equation, $f(x) = kx^2$ where k is a nonzero constant

quadrilateral a polygon with four sides

quartile one of the three values that separate an ordered data set into four equal parts; The second quartile Q_2 is the median of the data set. The first quartile Q_1 is the median of the lower half of the data set. The third quartile Q_3 is the median of the upper half of the data set. Note: A quartile also refers to the entire set of data in any quarter of the data.

quotient the result of division

radius (of a circle) a segment whose endpoints are the center of the circle and a point on the circle. The plural of *radius* is *radii*.

radius (of a sphere) a line segment joining the center of the sphere and a point on the surface of the sphere. The plural of *radius* is *radii*.

range the set of allowable outputs of a relation

range of a data set the difference of the maximum and minimum values in the data set

rate a ratio of two quantities measured in different units

rate of change the ratio of a change in one quantity to a change in a second quantity

ratio a comparison of two quantities by division

rational expression a fraction that includes expressions for the numerator or the denominator

rational number a number that can be expressed as a ratio $\frac{a}{b}$ where a and b are integers and $b \neq 0$; A rational number can be written as a fraction, a decimal, or a percent.

rational square root a square root that is a rational number

ray part of a line that begins from an endpoint and extends infinitely in one direction

reasonableness   the sense that an answer is correct, given the facts

reasoning   the series of thoughts and steps used to understand a problem, to create a plan to solve the problem, to reach a solution, and to accurately explain results

reciprocal   a number by which a given number must be multiplied to get a result of 1; also called the multiplicative inverse

rectangle   a parallelogram with four right angles; A square is a special type of rectangle.

reflection   a transformation of a figure by flipping it across a line or line segment, creating a mirror image of the figure

regular polygon   a polygon with all its sides congruent and all it angles congruent

relation   a mapping from a set of inputs to a set of outputs

relatively prime numbers   two or more numbers that have no common factors other than 1

remainder   the amount left over after dividing

repeating decimal   a decimal in which a digit, or a group of digits, other than zero repeats forever after the decimal point

replacement set   the given set of numbers that a variable may represent

representation   a way of displaying information, such as a model, a number, a graph, or an equation

rhombus   a parallelogram with four congruent sides; A square is a special type of rhombus.

right angle   an angle that measures 90°

right triangle   a triangle with a right angle

rigid transformations   transformations that do not change the size or shape of a figure

rise   the vertical change between two selected points on a line

rotation   the turning of a figure around a given point

round (v.)   to change a number to the nearest place value asked in a problem; For example, the result of rounding 532 to the nearest ten would be 530.

ruler   a tool to measure length, typically marked in centimeters or inches

run   the horizontal change between two selected points on a line

sale price   the price of an item after a discount

sales tax   a percent of the price of an item paid to a government when the item is sold

sample   part of a population

sample space   the set of all possible outcomes of an experiment

scale factor   the ratio of two corresponding sides in two similar figures

scalene triangle   a triangle that has no sides equal in length

scatter plot   a graph that displays data as points

scientific notation   a system of writing numbers as the product of a number that is greater than or equal to 1 but less than 10 and an integer power of 10

semicircle   half of a circle

sides of a polygon   the segments forming a polygon

similar figures   two figures in which each pair of corresponding angles is congruent and the ratio of the lengths of corresponding sides is constant

simple interest   interest earned at a fixed percent of the initial deposit, or principal amount

simple random sampling   sampling in which all members of the population have an equal probability of selection

simplest form of a fraction   a fraction in which the numerator and the denominator have no common factor other than 1 or −1

simplify a numerical expression   to find the value of a numerical expression

slide   the movement of a figure along a line without turns or flips, also known as translation

slope-intercept form of a linear equation
$y = mx + b$ where m is the slope of the line and b is the y-intercept

slope of a line the ratio of the vertical change, or rise, between any two points on the line to the horizontal change, or run, between the same two points

solution the answer to a problem or the process used to find the answer

solution of an open sentence a number that makes the open sentence true

solution set the set of all solutions to a given open sentence

solve to find the value(s) of the variable(s) that make an equation true

speed the ratio of distance traveled to time

sphere the set of all points in space that are a given distance from a point called the center

square a parallelogram with four congruent sides and four right angles

squared the result of the operation where a number has been multiplied by itself, such $5^2 = 5 \cdot 5 = 25$; When the area of a square is found, the dimensions are squared, and the area is expressed in units squared.

square of a number the product of a number and itself

square root a factor of a number that when multiplied by itself results in the number; The nonnegative square root is called the principal square root and is indicated by the square root sign.

square unit a square with sides of a particular side length, such as a square meter, used to measure area

standard form of a linear equation $Ax + By = C$ where A, B, and C are integers, and A and B are both nonzero

standard form of a number a number expressed using digits and place values

stem-and-leaf plot data display that lists the last digits (leaves) of the data values to the right of the earlier digits (stems)

straight angle an angle that measures 180°

strategy a technique used to solve a problem, such as working backward or drawing a diagram

stratified random sampling sampling in which the population is first organized into separate categories, and then each is sampled as an independent subpopulation

substitution the replacement of an equivalent value for another

subtrahend a number that is subtracted from another number

sum the result of an addition; The numbers added are addends.

supplement one of two supplementary angles

supplementary angles a pair of angles for which the sum of their measures is 180°

surface area the sum of the areas of all surfaces of a three-dimensional figure

surface area of a rectangular prism the sum of the areas of a prism's lateral faces and two bases

surface of a solid figure all of the polygons that are faces of the solid figure

survey a strategy for collecting data by asking questions of a group of people

systematic sampling sampling in which the population is ordered, and then members are selected at regular intervals through that ordered list

system of linear equations two or more linear equations using the same variables

tax a sum of money collected by a government

term a part of an expression that can be a number, a variable, or a product of numbers and variables

term in a pattern each number or object in a pattern

terminating decimal a decimal that has a finite number of nonzero digits to the right of the decimal point

term number the position of a term in a pattern

tessellation   a pattern of shapes that fit together with no overlaps or gaps and can extend to fill a figure

theoretical probability   the ratio of the number of favorable outcomes to the total number of possible outcomes

three-dimensional object   a figure with length, width, and height; often called 3-D

tip   an amount of money given to someone who provides a service

transformation (geometric)   a movement or change of a figure, such as a translation, reflection, rotation, or dilation

transformation (of an equation)   any change to an equation that results in an equivalent equation

translation   a sliding of a figure in a straight path without rotation or reflection

transversal   a line that intersects two or more lines in a plane

trapezoid   a quadrilateral with exactly one pair of parallel sides

tree diagram   a branching diagram used in probability to show outcomes of several events that occur one after the other

trend   a consistent pattern in data

triangle   a figure made up of three segments joined at their endpoints; Each endpoint is a vertex.

turn   the movement of a figure a certain number of degrees around a given point, sometimes called a rotation

two-dimensional shape   a figure with length and width, but no height; often called 2-D

two-way relative frequency table   a table that shows the relative frequencies of each data value in a two-way table

two-way table   a frequency table for two categorical variables

unbiased sample   a sample that is representative of the population

unit   an object or an amount used to measure, such as kilograms as a standard unit for mass

unit rate   a rate in which the second quantity in the ratio is 1

unlike denominators   denominators that are different in two or more fractions

upper bound estimate   an estimate for a problem that is greater than the actual solution could be

variable   a symbol that represents a value

variable expression   an expression consisting of one or more variables, one or more operations, and possibly one or more numbers; also called an algebraic expression

vector   a line segment with a direction indicated with an arrow

Venn diagram   a drawing that shows relationships among sets of numbers or objects

vertex   a point where two sides of a polygon meet. The plural of *vertex* is *vertices*.

vertical angles   two nonadjacent angles that share a vertex and are formed by two intersecting lines

vertical intercept   the value of the variable on the vertical axis at the point where a graph crosses the vertical axis

volume   a measure of space inside a figure

whole number   any member of the set $\{0, 1, 2, 3, 4, \ldots\}$

x-axis   in a coordinate plane, the horizontal line, or axis

x-coordinate   the first number in an ordered pair of numbers; also called the abscissa

x-intercept   the *x*-coordinate of a point where a graph intersects the *x*-axis

y-axis   in a coordinate plane, the vertical line, or axis

y-coordinate   the second number in an ordered pair of numbers; also called the ordinate

y-intercept of a graph   the *y*-coordinate of the point where the graph intersects the *y*-axis; also called the vertical intercept

Symbols

|	such that	$-a$	the opposite of a
$\in$	is an element of	a^n	a to the nth power
$\varnothing$ or {}	null or empty set	$\{\dots\}$	description or list of all elements in a set; roster notation
$\sqrt{a}$	principal square root of a		
$\sqrt[3]{a}$	cube root of a	%	percent
A'	A prime; the result of transforming point A	—	placed over a digit or a block of digits in a decimal to show that the digit or block of digits repeats
$\dots$	continuation of a pattern		
Q_1	first quartile	$\pm$	plus or minus
x_1	first value of x	$a:b$	ratio of a to b
π	pi	$\circ$	degree
( )	parentheses	$\overline{AB}$	line segment AB
[ ]	brackets	AB	length of line segment AB
$\approx$	is approximately equal to	$\overrightarrow{AB}$	ray AB
$=$	is equal to	$\overleftrightarrow{AB}$	line AB
$\neq$	is not equal to	$\triangle ABC$	triangle ABC
$\cong$	is congruent to	$\angle ABC$	angle ABC
$\sim$	is similar to	$m\angle ABC$	the measure of angle ABC
$<$	is less than	⌐	right angle
$>$	is greater than	$\parallel$	is parallel to
$\leq$	is less than or equal to	$\perp$	is perpendicular to
$\geq$	is greater than or equal to		
$\lvert x \rvert$	absolute value of x		

Properties

Real Number Properties

Let a, b, and c be any real numbers.

Addition Property of Equality	If $a = b$, then $a + c = b + c$ and $c + a = c + b$.
Addition Property: Addends with Like Signs	For all $a > 0$ and $b > 0$, $a + b = \lvert a \rvert + \lvert b \rvert$. For all $a < 0$ and $b < 0$, $a + b = -\lvert a \rvert + \lvert b \rvert$.
Addition Property: Addends with Unlike Signs	For all $a > 0$ and $b < 0$, $\quad$ If $\lvert a \rvert > \lvert b \rvert$, then $a + b = \lvert a \rvert - \lvert b \rvert$. $\quad$ If $\lvert a \rvert < \lvert b \rvert$, then $a + b = -\lvert b \rvert - \lvert a \rvert$.
Subtraction Property of Equality	If $a = b$, then $a - c = b - c$.
Substitution Property of Equality	If $a = b$, then a may be replaced with b in any expression or equation.
Multiplication Property of Equality	If $a = b$, then $c \cdot a = c \cdot b$ and $a \cdot c = b \cdot c$.
Division Property of Equality	If $a = b$ and $c \neq 0$, then $\dfrac{a}{c} = \dfrac{b}{c}$.
Distributive Property	$a(b + c) = ab + ac$

	Addition	Multiplication
Commutative Properties	$a + b = b + a$	$a \cdot b = b \cdot a$
Associative Properties	$(a + b) + c = a + (b + c)$	$(a \cdot b) \cdot c = a \cdot (b \cdot c)$
Inverse Properties	$a + (-a) = 0$ and $(-a) + a = 0$	$a \cdot \dfrac{1}{a} = 1$ and $\dfrac{1}{a} \cdot a - 1$, $a \neq 0$
Identity Properties	$a + 0 = a$ and $0 + a - a$	$a \cdot 1 = a$ and $1 \cdot a = a$

Absolute Value Equations

If $\lvert x \rvert = a$ for some positive number a, then $x = a$ or $x = -a$.

Properties of Exponents

Let a and b be nonzero real numbers. Let m and n be integers.

If n is a positive integer, then $a^n = a \cdot a \cdot a \cdot \ldots \cdot a$ (n factors).

Zero Exponent Property	$a^0 = 1, a \neq 0$
Negative Exponent Property	$a^{-m} = \dfrac{1}{a^m}, a \neq 0$
Product of Powers Property	$a^m \cdot a^n = a^{m+n}$

Square Root Properties

For nonnegative values of m, n, and p, if $m < n < p$, then $\sqrt{m} < \sqrt{n} < \sqrt{p}$.

Product Property	For real numbers a and b, $\sqrt{ab} = \sqrt{a} \cdot \sqrt{b}$ and $\sqrt{a} \cdot \sqrt{b} = \sqrt{ab}$.
Quotient Property	For real numbers a and b with $b \neq 0$, $\sqrt{\dfrac{a}{b}} = \dfrac{\sqrt{a}}{\sqrt{b}}$.

Reciprocal Properties

Reciprocal Property of Multiplication	For any nonzero real number a, $a \cdot \dfrac{1}{a} = 1$.

For all nonzero real numbers a and b, the reciprocal of $\dfrac{a}{b}$ is $\dfrac{b}{a}$.

For any nonzero real number a, $\dfrac{1}{-a} = \dfrac{-1}{a} = -\dfrac{1}{a}$.

For all nonzero real numbers a and b, $\dfrac{1}{ab} = \dfrac{1}{a} \cdot \dfrac{1}{b}$.

Division Properties

For any real number a and nonzero real number b, $a \div b = a \cdot \dfrac{1}{b}$.

For all real numbers a and b and nonzero real number c, $a + \dfrac{b}{c} = \dfrac{a}{c} + \dfrac{b}{c}$.

For all $a > 0$ and $b > 0$, $a \div b > 0$.

For all $a < 0$ and $b < 0$, $a \div b > 0$.

For all $a < 0$ and $b > 0$, $a \div b < 0$.

Properties of Order

Comparison Property of Order	If $a > b$, then $b < a$. If $a < b$, then $b > a$.
Transitive Property of Order	If $a > b$ and $b > c$, then $a > c$. If $a < b$ and $b < c$, then $a < c$.
Addition Property of Order	If $a > b$, then $a + c > b + c$. If $a < b$, then $a + c < b + c$.
Subtraction Property of Order	If $a > b$, then $a - c > b - c$. If $a < b$, then $a - c < b - c$.
Multiplication Property of Order, Positive Multiplier	If $a > b$ and $c > 0$, then $ca > cb$ and $ac > bc$. If $a < b$ and $c > 0$, then $ca < cb$ and $ac < bc$.
Multiplication Property of Order, Negative Multiplier	If $a > b$ and $c < 0$, then $ca < cb$ and $ac < bc$. If $a < b$ and $c < 0$, then $ca > cb$ and $ac > bc$.
Division Property of Order, Positive Multiplier	If $a > b$ and $c > 0$, then $\dfrac{a}{c} > \dfrac{b}{c}$. If $a < b$ and $c > 0$, then $\dfrac{a}{c} < \dfrac{b}{c}$.
Division Property of Order, Negative Multiplier	If $a > b$ and $c < 0$, then $\dfrac{a}{c} < \dfrac{b}{c}$. If $a < b$ and $c < 0$, then $\dfrac{a}{c} > \dfrac{b}{c}$.

Comparison Property of Rational Numbers

For nonzero integers a and c and positive integers b and d,

$\dfrac{a}{b} > \dfrac{c}{d}$ if, and only if, $ad > bc$.

$\dfrac{a}{b} < \dfrac{c}{d}$ if, and only if, $ad < bc$.

Properties of Proportions

Let a, b, c, and d be real numbers.

Means-Extremes Product Property	$\dfrac{a}{b} = \dfrac{c}{d}$ if, and only if, $ad = bc$, given that b and d are not 0.
Reciprocal Property	If $\dfrac{a}{b} = \dfrac{c}{d}$, then $\dfrac{b}{a} = \dfrac{d}{c}$, given that a, b, c, and d are all nonzero.

Formulary

Geometry

CIRCLE

circumference $\quad C = \pi d = 2\pi r$

area $\quad A = \pi r^2$

CONE

volume $\quad V = \frac{1}{3}Bh = \frac{1}{3}\pi r^2 h$

CYLINDER

volume $\quad V = Bh = \pi r^2 h$

surface area $\quad S = 2\pi r^2 + 2\pi rh$

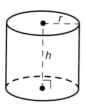

PARALLELOGRAM

area $A = bh$

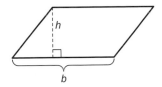

PRISM: CUBE

volume $V = s^3$

surface area $S = 6s^2$

lateral area of a prism $L = Ph$

PRISM: RIGHT RECTANGULAR

volume $V = lwh$

surface area $S = 2lw + 2lh + 2wh$

length of diagonal $d = \sqrt{l^2 + w^2 + h^2}$

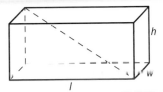

PYRAMID

volume $V = \frac{1}{3}Bh$

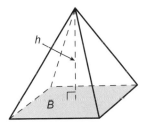

SPHERE

volume $V = \frac{4}{3}\pi r^3$

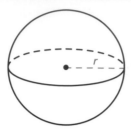

RECTANGLE

area $A = lw$

perimeter $P = 2l + 2w$

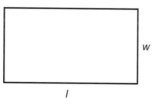

REGULAR POLYGON WITH n SIDES

perimeter of regular polygon $P = ns$

area of regular polygon $A = \frac{1}{2}aP$

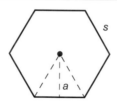

SQUARE

area $A = s^2$

perimeter $P = 4s$

TRAPEZOID

area $\quad A = \frac{1}{2}h(b_1 + b_2)$

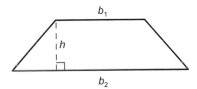

TRIANGLE: GENERAL

area $\quad A = \frac{1}{2}bh$

perimeter $\quad P = a + b + c$

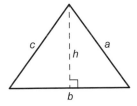

TRIANGLE: RIGHT

Pythagorean theorem $\quad a^2 + b^2 = c^2$

Coordinate Geometry

LINE

slope $\quad m = \dfrac{\text{rise}}{\text{run}} = \dfrac{\text{vertical change}}{\text{horizontal change}} = \dfrac{y_2 - y_1}{x_2 - x_1}$

linear equation: standard form
$Ax + By = C$

linear equation: slope-intercept form
$y = mx + b$

linear equation: point-slope form
$y - y_1 = m(x - x_1)$

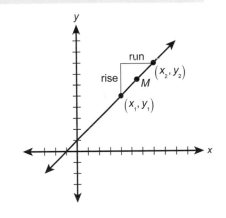

VERTICAL DISTANCE

same x-value $d = y_2 - y_1$

HORIZONTAL DISTANCE

same y-value $d = x_2 - x_1$

DIRECT LINEAR VARIATION

general formula $y = kx$ $k \neq 0$

QUADRATIC VARIATION

general formula $y = kx^2$ $k \neq 0$

Probability

SIMPLE THEORETICAL PROBABILITY

$$P(E) = \frac{\text{number of outcomes in event } E}{\text{total number of outcomes in sample space } S} = \frac{n(E)}{n(S)}$$

PROBABILITY OF MUTUALLY EXCLUSIVE EVENTS

$$P(A \text{ or } B) = P(A) + P(B)$$

RELATIVE FREQUENCY OF AN EVENT (EXPERIMENTAL PROBABILITY)

If n is the number of trials of an experiment or number of observations in a study, then the relative frequency of an event E is

$$P(E) = \frac{\text{number of times event } E \text{ has occurred}}{n}.$$

PROBABILITY OF INDEPENDENT EVENTS

For independent events A and B,

$$P(A \text{ and } B) = P(A) \bullet P(B).$$

PROBABILITY OF DEPENDENT EVENTS

For dependent events A and B,

$$P(A \text{ and } B) = P(A) \bullet P(B \text{ after } A)$$

where $P(B \text{ after } A)$ is the probability of B knowing that event A has already occurred.

GEOMETRIC PROBABILITY

$$P(E) = \frac{\text{area of region of success}}{\text{area of entire region}}$$

Statistics

MEAN

$$\overline{x} = \frac{x_1 + x_1 + \ldots + x_n}{n}$$

ABSOLUTE DEVIATION

The absolute deviation is the absolute value of the difference between a data value and the mean.

MEAN ABSOLUTE DEVIATION (MAD)

The MAD is the mean of all the absolute deviations. Calculate the absolute deviation for each data value and add. Then divide the sum by the number of data value.

MEANS-TO-MAD RATIO

$$\frac{|\overline{x}_1 + \overline{x}_2|}{\text{MAD}_{\text{larger}}}$$

MEDIAN

Arrange the values in order from least to greatest. For an

Odd number of values, use the middle value.

Even number of values, use the average of the middle two values.

MODE

The mode is the value that occurs most often in a set of data. If no one value occurs most often, then there is no mode for the set.

RANGE

$$range = maximum - minimum$$

Conversions

CONVERSION FOR LENGTH

English Units

1 ft = 12 in.

1 yd = 36 in.

1 yd = 3 ft

1 mi = 5280 ft

Metric Units

1 cm = 10 mm

1 m = 100 cm

1 km = 1000 m

CONVERSION OF CUBIC UNITS

English Units

$1 \text{ ft}^3 = 1728 \text{ in}^3$

$1 \text{ yd}^3 = 27 \text{ ft}^3$

Metric Units

$1 \text{ cm}^3 = 1000 \text{ mm}^3$

$1 \text{ m}^3 = 1,000,000 \text{ cm}^3$

SCALE FACTOR FORMULAS

If SA_F is the surface area of a figure that is enlarged or reduced with a scale factor, then the surface area of the scaled image, SA_I, is $SA_I = (\text{scale factor})^2 \cdot SA_F$.

General Applications

PERCENT OF CHANGE

$$\text{percent of change} = \frac{\text{amount of change}}{\text{original amount}} \cdot 100\%$$

SIMPLE INTEREST

$$I = Prt$$

where I is the amount of interest, P is the principal (the money you start with or your first deposit), r is the annual interest rate, and t is the time in years.

COMPOUND INTEREST

$$A = P(1 + r)^t$$

where P is the principal (the money you start with or your first deposit), r is the interest rate, and t is the number of years.

PERCENT ERROR

$$\text{percent error} = \frac{|\text{measured value} - \text{actual value}|}{\text{actual value}} \cdot 100\%$$

PERCENT OF TOTAL COST

$$\text{percent of total cost} = \frac{\text{individual cost}}{\text{total cost}} \cdot 100\%$$

FINAL PRICE FORMULA

$$\text{final price} = \text{pre-tax price} + \text{tax paid}$$

Illustrations Credits

All illustrations © K12 Inc. unless otherwise noted

Front cover Watercolor dragonfly. © Dobrynina Elena/Shutterstock.com

Back cover Watercolor cloud. © Noppanun K/Shutterstock

K¹² Summit Curriculum Computer monitor. © antpkr/Shutterstock; Tablet and phone. © Radu Bercan/Shutterstock

The Basics Paris guidebooks. © imagebroker/Superstock

Adding and Subtracting Rational Numbers Stocks. © iStockphoto/Thinkstock

Multiplying and Dividing Rational Numbers Zebras. © Steve Bloom Images/Alamy Stock Photo

Ratios and Rates Harley Davidson. © agf photo/Superstock

Proportions Lego model. © Sebastian Kahnert/dpa/Corbis

Expressions and Inequalities Balanced rock. © Tim Fitzharris/Minden Pictures/Corbis

Plane Figures Stained glass. © Meunierd/Dreamstime.com

Circumference of Circles and Area Crop circles. © Design Pics Inc./National Geographic Creative

Three-Dinensional Geometry Cargo ships. © donvictorio/Shutterstock.com

Statistics People at Flag Monument in Rosario, Santa Fe, Argentina. © Rodrigo Ruiz Ciancia/Getty Images

Probability Dartboard. © Ratina Thongteeka/Dreamstime.com